D1264342

Singer of Six Thousand Songs

A Life of Charles Wesley

Singer of Six Thousand Songs

A Life of Charles Wesley

by Elisabeth P. Myers

Drawings by Leonard Vosburgh

THOMAS NELSON & SONS

London *NEW YORK* *Toronto*

Books by Elisabeth P. Myers

Katherine Lee Bates: Girl Poet

F. W. Woolworth: Five and Ten Boy

George Pullman: Young Sleeping-Car Builder

Edward Bok: Young Editor

 Published in New York by Thomas Nelson & Sons and simultaneously in Toronto, Canada, by Thomas Nelson & Sons (Canada), Limited.

Library of Congress Catalog Card Number: 65-20772

Printed in the United States of America

Contents

Singer of Six Thousand Songs

A Life of Charles Wesley

1 | "Amen," Said Charles

A charred stick of wood hung over the front door of the new Rectory. It was an ever-present reminder to all in the house that some of the people of Epworth hated the Reverend Samuel Wesley, for the fire that destroyed the old Rectory had been set on purpose.

Charles had been only two on that dreadful night in 1709. He could not really remember that frightening crackle of burning thatch or the heat of the flames through which he was carried to safety. He could not remember, either, the dramatic rescue of his five-year-old brother, John, or that strange roll call his father took in the garden. He had heard about it all often enough, though, so he talked about it familiarly. Once, just before John left home to go to Charterhouse School, Charles had even dared tease his brother about being a "brand plucked from the burning."

"You'll have to lead a saintly life, Brother John," he said, "to prove to the Lord you were worth saving!"

Their mother, Susanna, had overheard Charles's taunt.

"The Lord moves in mysterious ways," she had said, her eyes flashing. "It may well be He has plans for John. It isn't up to you, my small son, to question Him."

It was hard for Charles not to question, though, when there was often not enough food to fill his stomach, nor any unpatched clothes to wear to church.

One day he had the rare luck of catching his busy

mother resting for a moment in a chair by the kitchen fireplace. He settled down on a stool at her feet and rested his head in her lap. As she stroked his hair gently, he dared to speak of what troubled him.

"Father is the Lord's spokesman," Charles said. "He loves the people of Epworth. Why do they destroy our crops and harm our cattle?"

Susanna did not answer for so long that Charles began to think she hadn't heard him. He was about to repeat his question when she began to speak.

"I, your mother, love you," she said, "but there are times when you do not want to do what I ask. There are times, indeed, when you do not obey."

Charles colored and he was glad his mother could not see his face.

"I can even remember times when you struck out at me with your fists," she continued. "Think of the Church of England as Mother Church and of the people as her children. Some of them do not like what they are told to do; so they, like you, hit out. That is why they set fire to our home—"

Her voice faltered as she spoke of the fire. Charles raised his head. He saw that Susanna's eyes were wet as she looked around the large, roomy kitchen.

"This place they cannot burn," she went on, again in control of herself. "The roof is tile, not straw, and the walls are brick. So now," she added, "they try to starve us, instead."

Charles sat up straight. "But why?" he asked again. "Father is not the Church!"

"He is, so far as Epworth is concerned," Susanna said. She patted Charles's shoulder and got up. "I must see what your sisters are doing. It is time Emilie and Molly, at least, were seeing to our supper. Martha and Anne, and I suppose the others, are at their spinning."

"Except Sister Hetty," said Charles. "She is in Father's study, reading some of her poetry aloud to him."

Susanna looked disturbed. "She would do better to realize poetry will not put bread in her mouth. But then, your father has written poetry in his life, too." She sighed. "It is a pity when one has bright daughters, and there is no money to do anything for them. As it is, we must rely upon your brother Samuel for help. Sammy, too, of course, writes poetry, but it is better than your father's and is helping him to succeed in London town."

Charles heard pride in his mother's voice, now, but he could not feel an answering pride. He did not even know this brother, who was the eldest of the nineteen Wesley children. He was seventeen years older than Charles and had already been away from home nine years at the time Charles was born. In all the time since then he had never had the money to come back to Epworth for a visit.

"Maybe someday I'll write something that will make you proud of *me*!" Charles said.

Susanna smiled. "You do not even know how to read yet," she said. "Next week you will be five years old. On the day after your birthday, I will undertake to teach you. You can show me then whether or not I shall have cause to be proud of you!"

She left Charles alone then, still sitting on the little hearth stool. He hugged his knees with his arms as he thought about what his mother had just said. In spite of the warmth of the peat fire, his teeth began to chatter. He knew that all his brothers and sisters had learned their letters in one day. Would he be able to do the same?

The morning after his fifth birthday, Charles went to his father's study. Susanna was waiting for him there.

"Shut the door, please, Charles," she said.

He closed it and leaned against it, his hands behind him pressing against the solid oak.

Susanna held out her hand to him. "Come, we will say a prayer together," she said.

They knelt side by side with bowed heads.

"Father, look upon this young mind with favor. Guide and bless this boy as he takes his first steps toward manhood, even as Your Son did before him. Amen."

"Amen," said Charles.

Susanna arose and seated herself behind the Reverend Samuel's desk. She motioned Charles to a seat in front of it. She handed him a hornbook. Charles knew it was the same one all his brothers and sisters had used, but he had never seen it before.

"Look at this quietly for a moment," Susanna said.

Charles took the book by its wooden handle. The cover was a thin layer of cowhorn. Inside it were sheets of stiff paper with black printing on them.

"Printed there are all the letters of the alphabet, both great and small," Susanna said. "On the first page, they are in order. On the following pages, they are mixed up. The first letter is A."

Over and over the alphabet they went. By midday, Charles could say it without looking at the book.

"Time out now for the noon meal," Susanna said, when the bells of St. Andrew's Church began to peal. "You've done very well, Charles. Why don't you go meet your father? The fresh air will do you good."

Charles placed the hornbook carefully on the desk. Then he rushed out to the kitchen, grabbed his coat from the hook where it hung, and went out of the door.

How good the frosty air felt after the stuffiness of the study! Charles took a deep breath, then exhaled for the pleasure of seeing the cloud he puffed out of his mouth. His boots clattered on the flagstones as he hurried up through the grove of bare-limbed lime trees toward the church.

About half way, he met the Reverend Samuel.

"And how did the morning go?" asked the Rector.

"Very well, Mother said," Charles told him proudly.

"Will you be ready to start on the Bible tomorrow, then?"

Charles shook his head. "I don't suppose so."

"No? Are you not so quick as Sammy and John, then?"

"Were *they* ready after one day? Well, then, I should be, too!" said Charles.

The Rector smiled. "That's the right attitude, my son," he said.

At two o'clock, Charles and his mother set to work again. By five o'clock, Charles, indeed, had mastered both the large and small letters. No matter where they were pointed out to him, he recognized them.

"Tomorrow," said Susanna, "we shall begin to read from God's holy word." She picked up a Bible and opened it. "We shall start with the first verse of the first chapter of the first book, and proceed only when you have the passage letter-perfect."

She put a ribbon in the Book to mark the place before she set it on the desk again. "Now, a closing prayer," she said, and sank to her knees.

Charles knelt beside her. He felt very pleased with himself. Just as Sam and John had done before him, he had learned all his letters in one day!

Susanna began, as she often did, to talk to the Lord as if He were in the room with her. "Thank You, Lord, for showing yet another of my children that perseverence and patience in well-doing bring their own satisfaction. May this virtue become a habit that will stand Charles in good stead all his life through."

"Amen," said Charles automatically. He got to his feet, eager to dash out and tell his sisters what he had accomplished.

Susanna put out a restraining hand as she, too, arose. "One last question," she said. "Do you know what that 'Amen' you said so easily means?"

"Means? Why, it's just what everybody says when a prayer is over!" said Charles.

"Like a period at the end of a sentence?" asked his mother, and then she smiled at her own words. "But you wouldn't know about that, either, since you haven't learned to read yet."

Charles moved his feet restlessly, wanting to get away, but he knew he must wait for his mother to dismiss him.

" 'Amen' means you have listened to what was said and approve of it," Susanna explained, "Do you understand?"

Charles nodded, and his eyes twinkled. "Amen!" he said.

2 Meetings with Susanna

Charles went to school to his mother for a year. Under her guidance, he read the Bible through, not just once but several times. He learned to write clearly and neatly and to do simple arithmetic as well. Only after Susanna had taught him all she could did he "graduate" to his father's tutoring.

The Reverend Samuel was devoted to the ancient languages, and from him Charles received a thorough grounding in Latin and Greek. The Rector did not stay close at hand to answer Charles's every question, though, as Susanna had. He set the boy a lesson "to be gotten by noon," then left him to go about the affairs of the parish.

All his life, Charles remembered the peace and quiet of those long mornings in his father's study. From where he sat on the window bench he could hear only the clank of the windmill in the nearby field or the subdued murmur of his sisters' voices as they went about their household tasks. If he raised his eyes from his book and looked out of the window, he could see the orderly rows of flax and, in the distance, the lines of dykes that controlled the water level in the flat Lincolnshire fields.

One day, the extreme quiet plus the warm sunshine streaming through the window were too much for Charles. He fell asleep, rousing only when his father returned at noon and shook him.

"For shame, Charles!" the Rector said. "There is a time for everything, and morning is not the time for sleep. Method is all important, my son—method and the disciplined life."

"I know," said Charles, who had heard the same words many times from his mother.

"And did you get your lesson before you fell asleep, or are both your time and mine to be wasted while you tardily apply yourself?"

"I hope I have it, sir," said Charles, crossing his fingers in a pagan ritual, rather than asking the Lord's intervention in such a trivial matter.

The Rector did not speak of Charles's unscheduled nap at the noonday meal, and he never mentioned it to Charles again. Charles confessed it, though, to his mother at their weekly tryst.

Every one of the Wesley children was granted an hour alone with Susanna every week. Charles's time was on Saturday from five to six, and had been ever since he was old enough to talk. Nothing was too trivial to tell his mother. She listened to everything without interruption, giving her advice only when it was asked.

Susanna was a religious woman, but she was also reasonable. She knew that things of the world were not unchanging, and she kept her mind always open to see both sides of a situation. She did not even believe that her husband, though he was God's spokesman in Epworth, was always right.

When Charles asked, "Will Father ever believe that I did not mean to fall asleep? 'The spirit was willing but the flesh was weak,' he told me. That's from the Bible, I know, but I don't remember from where."

"From the Book of Matthew," said Susanna. "The verse in which Jesus scolded his disciples for giving in to the temptation of falling asleep."

"Oh," said Charles, in a very small voice. "I remember now."

Susanna drew him to her in an unusually close embrace. "Take care never to fall asleep again when something is expected of you, and you will be the stronger for this one lapse," she said.

Often the Reverend Samuel had to leave the affairs of his parish to his curate and go himself to London. He was a member of Convocation, and his presence was required there. His dutiful attendance was also expected by his patrons, both noble and ecclesiastical, who provided him with small sums of money in return for favors he did them.

Before he had acquired these patrons, he had been obliged to spend some time in the debtors' prison at Lincoln. He never wanted that to happen again.

When the children were little, Susanna was too busy managing them and her household to pay attention to the way her husband's curate carried on in the Rector's absence. By the time Charles was six, though, some of the Wesley girls were grown up.

Susanna began to take a real interest in what was going on in Epworth, and she did not like what she saw. In particular, she did not like the dull and pointless sermons the curate preached.

Susanna knew good preaching when she heard it. Her father, Samuel Annesley, had been a prominent minister with a large popular following. No matter how long a sermon he preached, the people listened to every word.

Susanna's husband, Samuel Wesley, was a good preacher, too. Many of the people of Epworth did not like his firm stand on what the church expected of them, but that had nothing to do with what he said or how he said it.

The curate, though, could not attract enough people to fill the first three pews. Without Susanna and her children, he would have often preached to an empty church.

One day, after the curate had droned disjointed sentences for an hour, Susanna finally rebelled.

"I will not sit and listen to that man another Sunday," she told her children over their meal of spoonmeat and potatoes. "Starting this evening, I will give religious instruction myself, here in my own kitchen, for all those who care to come."

Charles paused with his spoon halfway to his mouth. "What will you tell them?" he asked.

"I shall tell them of the Lord and His ways, just as I tell you. I shall speak of the wonderful work that missionaries are doing, away off in the East Indies. I shall pray with them and for them."

Charles looked around the table as he spoke. He looked at his sisters' faces. The older girls—Hetty and Emilie, Martha and Mary and Anne—wore almost identical expressions of disapproval and even horror.

When Susanna finished, he waited for one of the girls to voice their feelings. No one spoke up at all. It was so quiet that Charles could hear everyone breathe.

"What are missionaries?" Charles asked into the uncomfortable silence.

"People sent out from their churches to preach and teach in foreign countries," Susanna explained. She looked at her daughters. "I can see," she said, "that you have learned the Fifth Commandment very well indeed. However, in obeying the Lord's order to 'Honor thy Mother,' you should not completely deny yourself the right to stand up and be counted. Have you *nothing* to say about my plan?"

The girls looked at each other, and an unspoken agreement was apparently reached, for Hetty suddenly spoke up.

"Religious meetings outside the church are not permissible, Mother," she said.

Susanna's eyes flashed. "They are not approved of, Hester," she said, "but as for being permitted—" She shrugged her shoulders.

"The curate will not like it, Mother," Hetty warned her.

"Well, I do not like what he is doing, either," Susanna said.

She got up from the table and walked over to the clothes rack. Putting her stiff black bonnet on her head, she tied the strings firmly under her chin. "I'm off to make the rounds of our nearest parishioners," she said. "Do you slick up the kitchen, for we will have company this night."

That Sunday evening and the next, Susanna welcomed some two hundred people who wished to join her and her family in religious observances. She did not try to preach, but encouraged people to speak simply and honestly of what troubled them. She read the Bible to them, and the sessions ended with all present saying the Lord's Prayer together.

The first people were filing quietly out of the door when the curate pushed his way rudely in among them. His black coat flapped, and his cravat was askew. He burst into the kitchen and shook his fist at Susanna.

"You are making a mockery of the Lord, woman!" he cried.

Charles moved quickly to his mother's side. She put her hand on his shoulder and pressed it. He understood he was not to say a word, no matter what happened.

"I honor the Lord by these observances, sir," she said quietly.

There was a babble of voices as people came to Susanna's defense. One burly man took up the poker and waved it threateningly. Charles could see the curate shrink back, as if afraid of a blow.

"I shall write your husband at once, Madam!" the curate said. "We shall see what he says about this breach of church rules."

Susanna was a small woman, but she stood up as straight as the poker her defender was brandishing. "Write my husband, by all means," she said, "but if you can show me any written rule that I am violating, I shall be surprised, sir."

Still spluttering, the curate faded back into the crowd and so out of the door.

The crowd was still muttering angrily, too. Susanna asked for the poker. With it, she banged against the fireplace.

"Everyone leave quietly, please," she said, and, to Charles's astonishment, everyone did as she asked.

When the room was empty of visitors, Susanna sat down in the chair beside the hearth. She motioned to her children to gather around her. When they, too, were quiet she spoke at last.

"Never be afraid to stand up for what you believe to be right," she said, and paused, as if waiting for a reaction.

" 'If God be for us, who can be against us?' you mean?" asked Charles, his eyes wide with sudden understanding.

His sisters looked at him with astonishment. Susanna, herself, seemed momentarily at a loss for words. When she did speak, her voice was hushed.

"That's it, exactly," she said.

This time there was no doubt in Charles's mind that he had made Susanna proud of him.

3 Arrivals and Departures

The Reverend Samuel did not forbid his wife to hold the religious meetings, though he did say he did not approve of them. Nevertheless, since the people seemed to benefit thereby, Susanna continued to be "at home" to all comers on Sunday evenings when her husband was in London.

Charles often stationed himself close to the door. He liked to greet the different people as they came in. He was interested to see how the men snatched off their caps the minute they entered, and how the women drew their shawls over their heads.

One night a complete stranger came in. Susanna was reading when he entered, so Charles put a finger on his lips and motioned the man to a place off to one side. The stranger smiled at him oddly, but obeyed Charles's gesture.

Charles stole glances at the unknown man from time to time. There was something familiar about him, yet Charles was sure he'd never laid eyes on him before. The stranger's clothes were grander than the Epworthians'. His full-skirted coat was shaped more sharply at the waist, and his shirt more richly ruffled. His boots, too, were of finer-grained leather, though they were covered now with mud and muck.

Susanna finished the chapter she was reading. As was her custom, she looked closely at the faces turned toward her. Suddenly she gave a little cry and, stepping down from her stool, made her way toward the man Charles had just admitted.

"Sammy! Sammy!" she cried, holding out her hands to the stranger.

All the people turned to watch the meeting between mother and son, for most of them knew that Samuel Wesley, the younger, had not been home for fifteen years.

Susanna led Sam forward.

"This is my eldest son, Samuel," she said. "He is a clergyman, and can talk to you better than I."

Sam spread out his hands in denial. "I need a pulpit for my preaching," he said, "and that I have not had for a long time, either."

"Samuel is an usher—a master—at Westminster School, London," Susanna explained.

"And a pretty fair poet, too, we hear tell," one of the older parishioners called, "good enough to be a friend of Alexander Pope!"

Charles could not stand being in the background any longer. He wriggled his way through the crowd to a place beside his brother.

"I'm Charles," he said, clutching Sam's sleeve. "Your brother!"

Sam put his hand on Charles's shoulder. "And a great lad you are too, Brother Charles!" he answered. "You and I will have to get acquainted, won't we?"

The nearest members of the congregation overheard the exchange between the brothers.

"Let us go now and leave them to their reunion, one of the throng said. "If you will just lead us in a closing prayer, Preacher Samuel."

Susanna folded her hands in front of her and bowed her head. The other people followed suit. Sam raised one hand in benediction.

"The Lord watch between us and thee, while we are absent one from another," he said.

Soon the Wesley family was alone, and then what an excited discussion broke out! Susanna seemed content to let her children do the talking. Charles noticed that she looked her eldest son over from head to foot, and that her eyes lingered lovingly on his face. What she saw apparently satisfied her, because she waited until everyone else stopped to take breath before she spoke.

"What is the particular occasion of your visit, Sammy?" she asked. "Did you see your father in London? Is anything amiss with him?"

"I saw Father," Sam said, "and had a long talk with him. His patrons are pleased with his latest batch of heroic couplets, and he says to tell you there will be a little more money forthcoming in consequence."

"Well, that's good news," Susanna said, "but nothing that could not have waited until his return."

"As to why I came, Mother," Sam went on, "it was to persuade you to let Charles go back with me to Westminster."

Charles gasped. "Me? To Westminster!"

Susanna was equally taken by surprise. "Charles? To Westminster?"

Sam nodded. "Charles to Westminster. I wish to sponsor him there. He will soon be eight years old, the age when I went off; the age John did, too."

Susanna sighed. "That's true," she said, and smiled at Charles a little sadly. "I suppose he is old enough."

Charles felt as if he would burst with questions. "What's Westminster like? Is it anywhere near Charterhouse School, where John is? Will I know enough to keep up with the other lads? Will you be one of my teachers?"

Sam held up his hand as if to dam up the flow of words.

"I'll take your questions one at a time," he said, laughing. "Westminster and Charterhouse are both in London, but you are not likely to see much of Brother John. I don't, from one year to the next. As to whether I shall teach you, surely I shall at some time or other. In any case, we will be often together."

"Will I be able to keep up with the other lads?" asked Charles again.

"Father seems to think so," Sam assured him. "He says you have been kept closely to your books for nigh unto three years now, and that you have learned to apply yourself well to your studies."

Sam smiled at him, then, and Charles wondered whether his father had told brother Samuel the story of his falling asleep that one time.

"As to what Westminster is like—well, that you will begin to find out for yourself very shortly. On Wednesday next we leave for London."

In the next few days, Charles looked at everything surrounding him at Epworth as if seeing it for the last time. After all, Sam had not returned home in fifteen years. Who knew when he, Charles, once away, would be back again?

He shared the great four-poster in his bedroom with Samuel now, a sharing he had not had to do since Jack went off to school. As he looked around the quiet little room, Charles wondered how it would be, instead, to share quarters with fifty other boys. The Rectory was always full of activity, of course, but since he was the only boy left at home, Charles had always had a place to retreat and be alone.

Charles climbed up to the church once more, too. It stood at the summit of the only hill in Epworth, and so from there Charles could overlook the whole town. He could see his home, enclosed though it was by a red brick wall ten feet high. He could see the feathery green of the lime trees and the brighter green of the gently sloping lawns.

He could see, too, just how the little rivers and the canal came together, and the rough farming country beyond. The arms of the windmills, turning slowly in the gentle breeze, seemed to be waving at him, and for a moment Charles felt the wild desire to wave back. He checked himself, though, telling himself he was too old for such nonsense.

On Wednesday, as he had promised, Samuel boosted Charles and his baggage up onto the roof of the London coach.

"We'll ride on top," he said, climbing up beside Charles, "and use the money we'll save to buy food and drink at stops along the way."

Charles sat clutching the wooden seat as the coachman whipped up the four horses, and they were off in a cloud of dust. The coach swayed and bumped along over the deeply rutted country roads. Sometimes the passengers were jerked so constantly that Charles's heels beat a tattoo on the boards behind his dangling legs.

When the horses pulled up at the first stop, Charles asked to look inside the coach. What a contrast the interior was to the place where he and Samuel were situated! The seats were covered with soft red velvet, the windows with silk hangings that could be drawn against the dust.

Nosegays of flowers were in little glass baskets that hung between the window frames. Their sweet scent perfumed the air, overcoming even the stench of the inn courtyard, where pigs and chickens wandered, squealing and squawking.

"Come, we'll have a chop and a flagon of nut-brown ale," Samuel said.

Charles slept, on and off, between the startings and stoppings of the coach along the rest of the route, but when they began to rattle over the streets of London he became alert. The noises seemed frightful to him, accustomed as he was to the quiet of the country. Street vendors shouted, street musicians fiddled wildly, dogs barked, horses neighed, and bells seemed to be clanging everywhere. Over all the confusion of noise, though, Charles could hear the master tolling of one great bell.

"What's that?" he asked Sam finally. "That deep, deep bell? It sounds almost like a sob, somehow."

Samuel looked at him curiously. "What an idea to have about St. Paul's!" he said.

Charles's heart skipped a beat. St. Paul's—the Cathedral Church of England! Until now, it had been only a name to him. Suddenly, it was real.

"Oh, Brother Samuel, will I really see St. Paul's?" he cried.

The day was rapidly drawing to a close, but the twilight air of London was remarkably clear. Samuel stood up to look off over the city.

"Yes!" he said excitedly. "You can see it now! The setting sun is gilding the dome of the Cathedral. Look quickly, Brother Charles!"

Charles climbed upon the seat to get greater height. There, standing out clearly against the darkening sky, was Sir Christopher Wren's masterpiece, finished, Charles remembered, just six years ago but forty-five years abuilding.

"Somehow I never thought about really *seeing* it," said Charles, when Samuel pulled him down again.

"Oh, come now," said Sam. "Save your rhapsodies for Westminster, which we'll be reaching shortly."

Charles felt the rebuke in his brother's voice, and thought perhaps he had not seemed grateful enough to Samuel for making this experience possible.

"Legend has it," Samuel went on more gently, "that the abbey was once visited by St. Peter in person."

Charles's eyes shone. He had heard very few stories in his young life, and sensed that his literary brother had many to tell.

"Is there more to the story?" he asked.

"St. Peter got a fisherman to ferry him across the Thames River. He entered the church, and as he entered it the walls suddenly glowed with a heavenly light, and a choir of angels burst into song. The fisherman fell to his knees and hid his face."

"What happened then?" asked Charles breathlessly.

"St. Peter raised him up and told him to go back to his

fishing, for he would catch more fish than he had ever dreamed possible."

"And did he?"

"He did," said Sam, "and ever since that time the Thames fishermen have given a tenth of their earnings to Westminster."

Charles clapped his hands. "Oh, that's a fine story, Brother Samuel!"

"And just finished in time," said Sam, "for ahead is the Dean's Yard, and our destination."

The time immediately following his arrival passed in a blur of bewilderment for Charles. He walked through what seemed an endless maze of cloisters, ate a frugal supper of black bread and broth in the monks' refectory, and was quickly assigned a truckle bed in an enormous, vaulted room.

The boys in the neighboring beds had time to say only a few words to him before the monitor came and blew out the lantern.

Charles lay awake for a long time on his hard, narrow bed. He listened to the breathing of the sleeping boys around him. He heard the rumble of London night traffic. Every fifteen minutes, over every other sound, he heard the chimes of the abbey. Finally, he remembered the legend Sam had told him, and thinking of St. Peter and the choir of angels, he was comforted and at last fell asleep.

4 | Early Days at Westminster School

"*Surgite!*"

The call echoed through the dormitory where Charles slept. He awakened, wondering for a moment where he was. As he rubbed his eyes to clear the sleep from them, he heard the nearby Abbey clock chime five times.

"*Surgite!*" came the call again, closer this time.

The command meant "Rise!" in the Latin language, but even if Charles had not known Latin he would have been in no doubt what it meant. Boys were tumbling out of their beds all around him.

Hurriedly, he threw back the stiff bed covers and got up, too. He reached for his clothes, but stopped when a nearby boy hissed at him.

"Down on your knees, before the monitor gets here!"

The warning came just in time. The King's Scholar was walking down the corridor between the lines of beds. Midway in the great room, he stopped and began in Latin the Collect for Grace in the morning.

"Oh Lord, our Heavenly Father, who has safely brought us to the beginning of this day—"

All the boys joined their voices with his to finish the prayer. As Charles said the familiar words, he thought of his mother and sisters at home. Perhaps they, too, were bowing their heads at this same time.

The thought made Charles feel warm all over, even

though the stone floor on which he knelt was cold and his nightshirt little protection.

"Now you can get dressed!" the boy next to Charles said, as soon as the prayer was over.

While Charles was struggling with the buckles that fastened his breeches at the knees, he stole glances at the monitor. He was a handsome lad, fourteen or fifteen years old.

Since Samuel, too, had been a King's Scholar, Charles knew this boy had won his position by competitive examination. The examiners had chosen him not only for his scholastic fitness but also for his character. After his election, all his expenses were paid for by the school, and he would be sure of being admitted to Oxford or Cambridge as soon as he was finished at Westminster.

"I'm going to be a King's Scholar someday," Charles promised himself, as he wiped the square buckles of his shoes between thumb and forefinger. "Then Brother Samuel will be free of having to support me!"

The monitor supervised the boys as they made their beds and swept their own quarters with bundles of rushes. He led them to the pump room, where they washed their hands and faces in icy-cold water they pumped for each other.

Charles could hear his stomach rumble, and he hoped breakfast would follow the washing-up. His hope was in vain, though, for the King's Scholar guided them into a chapel, where they were joined by hundreds of other boys.

Here the Headmaster, Dr. Freind, led them in Latin prayers, then dismissed them, not to breakfast but to classrooms.

"When do we get something to eat?" Charles whispered to the boy on the bench at his right.

"After a lesson in Greek and one in Latin—and more prayers," was the answer.

Charles turned to the boy on his left. "What time is breakfast?" he asked this time.

"Eight o'clock," came the response.

Charles groaned softly. Eight o'clock must be almost two hours away! As if to assure him he was right, the Abbey's chimes rang out six times.

Charles tried his best to apply himself to his work, though, because he wanted Samuel to be proud of him.

At last, eight o'clock sounded. The King's Scholars, two by two, led the way into the dining room. They waited until all the boys were standing beside their places, then went each to his own table, where he asked the Grace.

Charles was glad to see that the food was plentiful, though plain, consisting of great bowls of oat porridge and thick chunks of black bread, with small beer to wash it down. He ate heartily, for he was unsure at what hour the next meal would be served, and breakfast had been a long-time a-coming!

As he ate, Charles looked around the great hall, searching for Samuel. He saw his brother, finally, seated at what must be the Masters' Table, but he could think of no way of making Samuel aware of him.

No talking was allowed among the tablemates. During the meal, a Latin manuscript was read aloud, for entertainment or instruction, Charles wasn't sure which. He supposed this was a carry-over from the fourteenth century, when Westminster had been maintained by monks.

On the journey from Epworth, Samuel had told Charles something of the history of Westminster. It was one of the ancient public schools of England, having been taken over from the monks during the reign of Henry the Eighth, who first initiated the tradition of King's Scholars.

After breakfast, Charles tried to get across the hall to speak to his brother, but the monitor of his group held him back.

"Where are you going?" he asked in Latin.

Charles started to answer in English, but the Scholar stopped him.

"Hasn't anyone told you? We speak nothing but Latin here!"

Hastily, Charles explained what he wanted, but it was no use.

"There's no time to indulge yourself now," the Scholar told him. "You will have lessons until dinner time at twelve o'clock. After dinner you will have 'construes'—translation from Greek or Latin into the King's English—for two hours."

Charles looked distressed. "Don't we have any time to just *breathe?*" he asked.

The Scholar looked at him sternly for a moment. Then his glance softened, and he smiled a little.

"It always seems like a tough schedule to lads fresh from home," he said. "But—yes. After construes, you'll get a short breathing spell. Then if you see your brother, you can speak to him."

"And after the breather, what?" asked Charles.

"Studies until supper time. After supper an hour for translation from English into Latin. Then bedtime at eight o'clock."

Charles did not get a chance to speak to Samuel that day nor for many days thereafter. By the time they did meet, Charles was quite used to the routine of the school and felt as if he'd been there always.

"Everything going all right for you, Brother Charles?" Sam asked him.

"I have no complaints, Brother Samuel," he replied.

"I've heard no complaints about you, either," said Sam.

"And you never will!" Charles assured him.

Charles spoke too soon, though, for the very next afternoon, during the breather, he got into trouble.

At the public schools of England in those days, there were no playing fields or recreational facilities. The boys did not even know the meaning of the word "game," except as it referred to the wild life in the forests and fields that only noblemen were permitted to hunt.

By instinct, though, they did know how to use their fists, and how to use sticks to give beatings, too. In the early years of George the First, in fact, fisticuffs was a popular pastime, and one which the boys of Westminster enjoyed, too, when they could.

Charles did not know how to fistfight before he entered Westminster School, but he learned rapidly and soon could hold his own with anybody his own size. The King's Scholars were usually around to monitor the fights that took place, and Charles noticed they always insisted that the opponents be evenly matched.

One day, however, it happened that all the King's Scholars had been called to attend a meeting. Charles, in the midst of his own group of friends, was rather enjoying not being supervised for a change. He imagined most of the other lads felt the same way, until suddenly he heard a scream from one corner of the big yard.

"Please don't! Please don't!" a frightened voice called.

Thinking only that he wanted to see what was going on, Charles pushed his way through the throngs of boys to the spot where all the commotion was.

"What's all the fuss about?" he asked.

"See for yourself," the boy he'd questioned replied, jerking a thumb in the direction Charles was to look.

Charles saw a little boy lying on the ground. Several older boys were standing over him, some kicking him, some beating him with sticks.

"Cease that, you bullies!" Charles shouted.

With fists doubled, he lowered his head and charged toward the punishing group.

"He's a Jacobite!" one of the tormentors cried, but he stopped using the stick he held in his hand when he saw Charles's angry face. "He doesn't believe our George should be King of England!"

"Well, that doesn't give you the right to beat him as if he were a beast!" cried Charles. "Let him up, I say, and I'll fight each one of you for him!"

Laughing scornfully, the little boy's tormentors turned on Charles instead. Fighting with a ferocity that surprised himself, Charles hit out again and again. He gave one boy a black eye and bloodied another boy's nose before a King's Scholar pushed his way into the crowd and stopped the battle.

"How did this disgraceful exhibition get started?" the monitor asked.

"He said he'd fight us all!" one of the troublemakers said, pointing at Charles.

The Scholar looked at Charles. "Did you?" he asked.

"Yes, sir," said Charles, because he *had* said just that. "But—"

"No *buts!*" said the King's Scholar.

Charles looked around for the little boy whose cause he had championed, but he was nowhere to be seen.

"I'll see that you get one hundred extra lines to construe," the monitor said sternly. "Now, everybody go in quietly. It is time you were with the Greek master."

That evening Samuel came to see Charles, who was struggling with the extra lines of his punishment lesson.

"I do not like the tale I hear of you, Brother Charles," Samuel said sadly. "Our mother would be pained if she knew."

The thought of his mother's distress made Charles feel a real pang in his heart, too. He wondered if he could tell Samuel why he felt he had to fight, but then he knew he couldn't.

"I'm sorry it happened, Brother Samuel," Charles said. "More sorry than you know."

"Then it will not happen again," said Samuel. He laid a hand forgivingly on Charles's shoulder. "So we'll say no more about it."

Charles could not forget it, though; and, as he had on his first night, he lay awake after he got to bed.

He heard the clock strike all the four quarters of the first hour as he lay there staring into the darkness. All around him, boys were sleeping peacefully. Then, suddenly, the gleam of a lantern broke the blackness, and two figures appeared beside his bed.

It was the King's Scholar who had stopped the fight and the little boy Charles had delivered.

"James Murray has something to say to you, Charles Wesley," the Scholar said. "Speak up, James."

"Oh, Mr. Wesley," the little boy cried, "I am so sorry I ran away. I did not know you would get into trouble over me, truly I didn't. I—I'll make it up to you some day. You'll see!"

It was the first time Charles had been called "Mr. Wesley," and he liked the sound very much. It made him feel old and important.

"Oh, that's all right," he said, thinking that now he'd do it all over again if he had to.

"It is not all right," the Scholar said. "You have been wrongly punished, and I will see that a public apology is made to you at breakfast tomorrow morning."

The Scholar and the little boy then went away. Charles watched the lantern as it bobbed along the corridor. Before it reached the end of the room, he was asleep.

5 Charles Has a Visitor

Charles's championship of James Murray and the stoicism with which he accepted unjust punishment made him something of a hero with the boys at Westminster School. Since he was also a very good classical scholar, he had the favor of the masters, too. Indeed, the Headmaster, Dr. Freind, was so taken by Charles's entire character that he oftentimes invited the boy to literary gatherings under his roof.

At such affairs, Charles met many of the great figures of the age: poets and satirists like Alexander Pope and Jonathan Swift, essayists like Joseph Addison and Richard Steele, playwrights like John Gay. Under the influence of such men, Charles began to write poetry and epigrams, and even to try his hand at playwriting.

From an interest in playwriting, Charles also acquired an interest in acting. The boys at Westminster did not have much chance to practice that sort of relaxation, but every year the school did put on a play. The Westminster Play was, indeed, a tradition—usually written by the masters and acted out by the boys.

Charles, who had not only good looks but a fine voice, nearly always had a place in the cast. In 1719, when he was twelve years old, he wrote the play and acted the main part as well.

The fame of the Westminster Play reached far and wide, and in the audience were always members of the literary world. Therefore, when Charles was told that a fine gentleman was waiting to talk to him, he was not really surprised. After all, he knew many of the gentlemen. It would only be friendly of one of them to wish to congratulate him.

"Who is it?" he asked the messenger boy. "Mr. Johnson? Mr. Matthew Prior, perhaps?"

The messenger boy shook his head. "Whoever he is, he's Irish," he replied.

"Irish? Mr. Steele?"

"No. I know Mr. Steele. I never saw this man before."

"Where will I find this fine gentleman, then?" Charles asked, trying not to show the curiosity he felt.

"In Dr. Freind's reception hall," the boy replied.

Charles made his way through the cloisters and across the Dean's Yard to Dr. Freind's rooms. His heart was beating rapidly. He had been to the Headmaster's rooms often, but now with every step he took he could feel his excitement mounting. He stopped at the entrance to the reception hall to catch his breath and to steal a glimpse at his visitor.

The man with Dr. Freind was a complete stranger to Charles. He was a very stout man, with an elaborate, flowered waistcoat that only served to emphasize the roundness of his figure. On his head, he wore the handsomest wig Charles had ever seen—pure white, very silky, and dressed with corkscrew curls that fell to his shoulders.

Charles advanced into the room and bowed deeply. The Headmaster bowed his head only, as did the gentleman with him.

"Mr. Wesley, sir," said Dr. Freind, with a twinkle in his eye, "may I present—Mr. Wesley."

Charles was so surprised by this introduction that he could only stare at the Headmaster.

The visitor chuckled. "I am your kinsman, Garrett Wesley, Charles," he said.

Charles bowed again. "How—how do you do, sir?" he

asked politely, but his mind was busy trying to think what Garrett Wesley could want with him.

Garrett Wesley, Charles realized, must be from the Irish branch of the family. That branch had settled near Dublin and grown prosperous there, in contrast to the English branch of which the Reverend Samuel was now the head.

"Well!" said the Headmaster. "Why don't you kinsmen sit down over there and get acquainted?" With one hand, he indicated the brocade-covered sofa before the huge fireplace. "I shall have a servant bring you some refreshment."

Charles and Garrett Wesley sat down together, as bidden. Garrett Wesley settled back and made himself comfortable.

"I wish to congratulate you on a fine performance," Garrett Wesley said.

For a moment, Charles couldn't even think what performance his kinsman meant. The Westminster Play seemed as far off as a dream, in the face of the present startling situation. "Thank you, sir," he said."

"It is really quite wonderful how much license these Church of England schools allow the scholars," Garrett Wesley went on.

"License, sir?"

"Was playacting part of your upbringing, my young friend? As I remember my cousin, Samuel, he was much too straight-laced to permit *that* in his household!"

Charles felt acutely uncomfortable at Garrett Wesley's words, because of course there never had been time for playacting in the Samuel Wesley household.

"Everyone was always too busy for playacting at home," Charles said, "but Father did find time to write verses; I think he might have written a play, if he had wanted to. Brother Samuel did, you know, one that was acted here a few years ago."

"Ah, yes," said Garrett Wesley. "I have heard of your brother Samuel. I have heard of him, in fact, from the same person who told me of *you*."

"Who—who was that, sir, if I may ask?"

"The Reverend Jonathan Swift," Garrett Wesley replied, and smiled. "A prime example of the literary clergy, if I may say so."

Once again, Charles was too surprised to speak. He had not realized that the famous poet and satirist was a minister of the Church of England.

"Yes," continued Garrett Wesley, "he is a near neighbor of mine at Dangan, close to Laracor, or he is when he is in Ireland."

"And he told you of Brother Samuel and me, sir?" asked Charles, prompting his kinsman to get on with what he had to say. "It was kind of him to mention *me,* for after all, I am only a boy."

"You are too modest," said Garrett Wesley. "The Reverend Swift talked so glowingly of you that I came to see you for myself. Your Headmaster thinks highly of you, too. He tells me you not only know how to use your brains but also your fists!"

Charles felt the blood rise in his cheeks. There had been several times since his fight for James Murray that he had had to defend himself with his fists, and somehow word of the battles always got around the school.

"You seem to be, in short," said Garrett Wesley, "the kind of kinsman I'd like to reward."

Charles could feel excitement mounting in him again at the word "reward." What kind of reward would it be?

"Thank you, sir," was all he could think of to say.

"As you may have heard, I am a very rich man. My wife is an invalid—"

"I'm sorry, sir."

"And we have no heirs. I am looking for someone to inherit my estates and my fortune."

Now Charles was so excited he could scarcely breathe. He could feel the perspiration gathering under his stiff collar and trickling down his back. He clenched and unclenched his fists, trying to calm himself.

"You may be just the one I'm looking for," said Garrett Wesley. "I'm not absolutely sure, yet, but sure enough to offer to pay your expenses here for a while. By the time you're ready for a University, I'll have made up my mind."

Charles's heart gave a great leap. Now Samuel would be able to save the money he'd been paying for Charles's schooling. He could send that amount back to Epworth to make things easier for Susanna and the girls.

"That would be wonderful, sir!" Charles said, gripping Garrett Wesley's hand.

His kinsman nodded. "Meanwhile, you be thinking whether you *want* to accept my offer, if I decide to make it!"

As if on a stage cue, the Headmaster appeared, followed by a servant with a laden tray. On it were fancy cakes of the variety Dr. Freind always offered his literary friends, and a steaming pot from which came an appetizing odor unfamiliar to Charles.

"And how have you fared?" asked Dr. Freind. "Have you had a chance to get acquainted?" he added, rubbing his hands together.

"Yes, sir," said Charles, and Garrett Wesley nodded.

"Well, then," said the Headmaster, "we're all ready to have some hot chocolate and cakes." He winked at Charles. " 'Tis probably the first time you've had hot chocolate, Charles, but 'twon't be the last. Not," he added, laughing, "if you become Mr. Garrett Wesley's son and heir!"

Charles was grateful when Dr. Freind turned his attention to his more distinguished guest. When the plate of cakes was passed to him, Charles took one, but it tasted like sawdust in his mouth. Garrett Wesley's son and heir? Was that what he, Charles Wesley, would be?

6 Charles and Westminster Abbey

Charles's diet of classical studies was lightened by other things than the Westminster Play. The Headmaster was well aware that the boys in his school had to be prepared for life outside the cloistered walls. Since Westminster Hall was a close neighbor, Dr. Freind saw to it that his scholars attended everything special that went on there.

History came to life for Charles whenever he stepped beneath the Hall's magnificent open-timbered roof. Every important state trial had taken place there since the year 1099, when King William Rufus held his first court in the just-completed building. There Guy Fawkes was condemned to be hanged, drawn and quartered for his plot to blow up the buildings of Parliament when King James I was inside. There Charles I received his death sentence, and Oliver Cromwell had himself declared Lord Protector of England.

Far more important than Westminster Hall in Charles's life, however, was Westminster Abbey. The Abbey chimes had comforted him on his first night in London, and they had regulated the movements of his school week ever since.

Charles had begged permission to visit the Abbey early in his first week at the school. He had gone alone to the huge gray building, approaching the great west doors almost fearfully. Just inside, he exclaimed aloud, and was startled to hear his voice echo.

Until now, the only church he had known was little St. Andrew's, where his father was rector. It could, Charles thought, be put down in the middle of Westminster Abbey and hardly be noticed at all!

Westminster Abbey soon became as familiar to Charles as St. Andrew's, though, because on Sunday it filled his waking hours. The whole school attended Matins, the service of public morning prayer, there, and Evensong, the service of evening prayer, as well.

The interval between the services was spent by the boys in translating into Latin the English sermon they had just heard. The little boys were allowed to put it into Latin prose, but the older ones were expected to transform it into Latin verse.

Charles much preferred the exercise in versification. It was the kind of thing his father had delighted in having him do; Samuel Wesley was determined to transform the Holy Scriptures not only into Latin, but into Hebrew verse.

The time of Evensong was Charles's favorite hour of the week. The whole school marched in silent processional down the great center aisle toward the high altar. Each of the boys carried his own candle. The flames flickered, casting their moving light on the huge pillars which soared up into the darkness.

Then, when all the boys were kneeling, an anthem would rise from the shadowy recesses of the choir stall. Charles never heard the choristers without a catch in his throat, for it seemed to him that angels were singing.

"Someday," he told himself over and over, "someday perhaps I shall write a song good enough for the Westminster Choir to sing!"

Charles soon found out that Westminster Abbey was much more than just a church where services were held. From William the Conqueror onward, every British sovereign had been crowned in the Abbey except Edward V, and the coronation chairs stood in Edward I's Chapel, where boys like Charles could see and touch them. Many kings and queens were buried in the Abbey, too, and indeed it sometimes seemed to Charles that he could not take a step without walking on someone's grave.

The Abbey was, in fact, crowned with tombs and memorials of many famous British subjects as well as the kings and queens. The north transept of the church was a burial ground of statesmen. The south transept was reserved for the graves of literary men, among them Geoffrey Chaucer, Edmund Spenser, and John Dryden.

The so-called "Poets' Corner" was a favorite haunt of Charles's, for it, like Westminster Hall, was steeped in history. William Shakespeare was not buried there, but there was a memorial tablet to him. Brother Samuel had pointed out to Charles that the lines from the play *The Tempest* were wrongly quoted, and ever afterwards just seeing the tablet made Charles smile.

Although Charles was familiar with the Abbey, he had no personal ties with any of the writers who were buried there. That is, he did not until Midsummer Day, 1719. At midnight, Joseph Addison, whom Charles had often met and talked with in Dr. Freind's rooms, was laid to rest in Henry the Seventh's Chapel.

All but the very youngest of the Westminster School boys were awakened and marched over to watch the burial. They were lined up in the carved oak stalls over which the banners of the Knights of the Bath hung. The banners moved gently in the drafty room, sending an occasional musty odor downwards. Ever afterwards, when Charles smelled such an odor, he thought of this midnight ceremony in the Abbey and shivered.

The King's Scholars stood around the open grave with tapers in their hands, parting ranks only when the pallbearers slid the body of the great essayist into his final resting place. The Dean of the Abbey intoned the burial service, and the people who crowded the chapel joined him in prayers for the soul of the dead man.

When the ritual was over, Charles walked out of the Abbey as if he were in a dream. All over the city of London the bells were tolling for Joseph Addison. The air rang with the sound of little bells and big bells, deep tones and high tones. Over them all, Charles could hear, as he had the night he arrived in London, the mighty roll of the bells of St. Paul's.

Such experiences with the beauty and solemnity of the Church of England ritual made Charles conscious of the need for ceremony in the practice of religion. He began to see why his father's curate had objected to Susanna Wesley's Sunday evening meetings. He knew why his mother had felt they were necessary, and he was sure she was right. The fact was that the curate had not used the Church of England ritual as it should be used.

Charles spoke of this realization to Sam.

"You arrived in the midst of one of Mother's prayer meetings, Brother Samuel," he said. "Do you think she was wrong to hold them outside the church?"

Sam seemed to weigh Charles's question carefully before answering. "Our father did not see that there was anything wrong in them," he finally said, "although he properly believes that the church is the place for religious gatherings. Sometimes, as you will find out, circumstances alter cases." Sam sighed. "Unfortunately, many clergymen of the Church of England share our Epworth curate's fault, Charles. They are making organized church services so dull that they are driving the people away from them."

Charles felt a sense of shock. He thought of the immense lift of the spirit he received whenever he attended a service in the Abbey, and was sad that everyone in England could not share such an experience.

"But that's not right!" he cried.

Charles's blue eyes were shining with the fervor of his

belief. He had pushed a hand through his blond hair and a lock of it stood upright. Sam smiled and reached out to smooth the unruly strands back into place.

"Of course, it's not right," Sam said gently. "Brother Charles, I love the Church of England with all my heart and soul. I am doing what I can to influence those around me to love it, too."

Those words of his brother stayed with Charles, recurring to him at odd times during the day, always bringing with them a surge of affection for the man who had spoken them. Samuel stood, indeed, in place of mother and father for Charles now, and Charles wanted nothing so much as to make Samuel proud of him.

7 Experiments and Decisions

Charles's father, the Reverend Samuel Wesley, had given him a good grounding in Latin and Greek, but it was Vincent Bourne, the eccentric classics master, who made Charles a foremost classical scholar.

Mr. Bourne was in charge of the study hall one Sunday when Charles made his first attempt to translate the sermon he had just heard into Latin verse instead of Latin prose. The Master was wandering up and down between the long study tables, giving help when help was needed. He stopped beside Charles, who was biting the end of his quill pen and staring up at the ceiling.

"Dreaming with your eyes open, young sir?" asked the Master.

Charles started. "Oh, no, sir!" he said, wondering how he could explain to the odd Vinny Bourne. "I was trying to—well—fit the words I have in mind into the necessary rhyme form."

"Into the heroic couplets, I suppose you mean," said Vincent Bourne. "The di *da,* di *da,* di *da,* di *da,* di *da* that is so popular?"

Charles smiled at the Master's singsong. "Yes, sir."

"Were you looking for inspiration on the ceiling? I thought it was a rather good sermon myself. Well worth heroic translation!"

That's just it, sir! I think it deserves something more—

oh, less *set*—than the heroic verse form, I guess I'm trying to say."

"Irregular verse, you mean?" Now it was Vincent Bourne who sounded excited. "Well, if that is what you want to do—do it!"

"But will it be acceptable?" asked Charles.

He was always conscious of the need to do what was correct, scholastically speaking. Brother Samuel expected only the best from him, and he owed his very existence at Westminster to his brother. Now, of course, Garrett Wesley was paying his way, but Samuel was still the one for whom he worked.

"It certainly would be to me," said Vincent Bourne. "What is your name, young sir?"

"Charles Wesley, sir," said Charles.

"I'm Vincent Bourne," said the Master.

"I know, sir," Charles said, and blushed.

Everyone at Westminster, Charles was sure, knew who Vincent Bourne was. He was the butt of many schoolboy jokes, because he cared nothing about his personal appearance. His hair hung in greasy locks to his shoulders, and his clothes were always spotted and soiled. All he cared about was teaching and writing poetry. Since he was excellent at both, he was considered a valuable addition to Westminster School in spite of his looks.

Vincent Bourne seemed to know what was going through Charles's mind. "I suppose you do," he said, "but what you don't know are the things that count."

"Yes, sir," said Charles.

"You interest me," Mr. Bourne went on. "I am going to ask that you be transferred to my class. At present, I don't have a boy in it who cares a fig for writing verse. I have a feeling I could interest *you* in different meter forms. Could I?"

Charles felt at a loss for words. In an age when heroic

couplets were considered correct for all poetic thought, should he dare be different? Wasn't what was good enough for the great Pope good enough for him?

"What's troubling you?" asked Vincent Bourne. "You said you thought today's sermon deserved a different verse form than you knew how to give it. Are you afraid to experiment?"

The word "afraid" always aroused a fighting-back spirit in Charles. "No!" he said.

"Good," said the Master. "Tomorrow morning, report to me. We shall see if you mean what you say!"

From the first day, Vincent Bourne's classes proved challenging to Charles. His admiration for the Master's intelligence grew with every contact. Apparently the admiration was two-sided, because it was not long until Vincent Bourne asked Charles's help in getting out a quarto volume of Latin poetry.

"Some of your verse can be included in the book," the Master told Charles. "Wouldn't it be exciting to see something you have written in print?"

"Oh, of course it would!" said Charles.

Quite naturally, Sam was pleased that Charles was taking such an interest in verse-writing, though he did not himself have any desire to break away from the classic form of the day.

"Why do you want to be different?" he asked Charles, when he saw the unconventional verses Charles was contributing to Vincent Bourne's book.

"There are just some thoughts you can't express in the 'di *da,* di *da,* di *da,* di *da,* di *da*' meter," said Charles, aware that he was echoing Vincent Bourne.

"No thoughts I can't express," said Samuel. "But no matter. I'm proud of the way you're progressing here at Westminster, Charles. So, I understand, is Garrett Wesley."

Charles had proudly told his brother all about Garrett

Wesley's visit, since the Irishman's offer relieved Samuel of responsibility for Charles's schooling. As the years passed by, though, Garrett Wesley never had come back to see Charles. If the money for his keep had not kept arriving, Charles would almost have been inclined to believe he had dreamed the whole affair.

That was why Charles now felt as if his heart had leaped into his throat. He swallowed with difficulty, forced once more to face the matter.

"Do you suppose our kinsman will really ask me to be his heir, Brother Samuel?" he asked, fighting down the feeling of panic.

"I'm sure I do not know, Brother Charles. Dr. Freind tells me, though, that Mr. Wesley insists upon detailed monthly reports of your progress, so he certainly has not dismissed you from his mind."

"Oh," said Charles. "Oh."

Charles's progress continued to be good, and in 1721, on his fourteenth birthday, he was appointed a King's Scholar.

This was the honor Charles had striven for since his first morning at Westminster. When he, too, had the opportunity of monitoring a group of new boys, he remembered exactly how he had felt when he was a stranger.

Being in charge of younger children was a completely new experience for Charles. At home, he had always been the baby, somewhat spoiled by his older sisters. When he came to Westminster, how grateful he was to have Samuel there to turn to for direction and support.

All these things Charles remembered when he finally became a King's Scholar. He determined that he would act in the stead of an older brother to the new boys, so that they would be proud to follow him.

The result was that Charles endeared himself to the whole school. Therefore, when in 1725 a new school Captain had to be elected, he was chosen over the four hundred other scholars for the top position.

Now there was no question which University Charles would attend. The Captain of Westminster School automatically received a scholarship to Christ Church College at Oxford. The scholarship would not keep him in luxury, but it would suffice for his living.

At the close of that year, Garrett Wesley returned to Westminster School. Once again, Charles was summoned to the Headmaster's rooms to meet his kinsman. Once again they sat together on the brocade sofa.

They looked at each other. Charles thought Garrett Wesley looked much the same, except that he was even stouter and his face was somewhat more highly colored. Charles knew that he, himself, had altered considerably. He certainly wasn't a small, timid boy any more!

"Well," said Garrett Wesley, clearing his throat. "You've changed, young Charles."

Charles's lips quirked, but he did not allow himself to actually smile. "Yes, sir, I suppose I have," he said.

Garrett Wesley sat forward, legs apart, his hands resting palm downward on his knees.

"I've just come from Epworth," he said.

"From Epworth!" said Charles. "Did you see my parents, sir? Are they well?"

"They are well. I told your father, Charles, that I would like to make you my heir."

Charles's heart began to race crazily. The moment he had waited for and dreaded had come.

"He sent you this letter," Garrett Wesley went on, handing a piece of paper to Charles. "I hope your father merges his desires with mine!"

Charles took the paper, noticing that it was sealed with wax on which was the imprint of his father's ring. He broke the seal, then looked at his kinsman for permission to read.

Garrett Wesley got to his feet. "I'll go for a short stroll in the Dean's Walk," he said.

Quickly Charles scanned his father's words. Then he went back to the beginning and reread more slowly, trying to see the unspoken message between the lines.

Epworth Rectory
June 1725

Dear Son Charles:

Our kinsman, Garrett Wesley, has informed me that he wishes to make you heir to his estates and fortune.

Acceptance, of course, means that you would live in Ireland. You would become a member of the landed gentry, certain of taking your place among the great men of the time, for with great wealth anything is possible.

The alternative is certain poverty, for no one of the English Wesleys can help you further. Whatever you make of your life will be your doing and yours alone.

The decision must be yours, and may the Lord God guide you in your choice.

Your affectionate father,
SAMUEL WESLEY

Charles folded the letter carefully, being sure to follow the original creases, then as carefully unfolded it again to look at his father's words once more.

"The decision must be yours. The decision must be yours."

The challenge of those words beat over and over in Charles's mind, seemingly in time to his quickened heart beat and labored breathing. He seemed to see the whole past fourteen years roll in front of his eyes. He thought of his parents, of his sisters and his brothers. He thought of Samuel, in particular, Samuel who had been all the family he had seen in almost ten years. Could he leave England, perhaps never to see Samuel again? Did he really want to be a country squire, when it came down to that?

Charles had, of course, unconsciously been considering such questions ever since Garrett Wesley's surprising first visit. Now the answer came in a flash. It was "No." He did not want to be a country squire. What he did want was to go on to Oxford and see what opportunities beckoned from there. After all, anybody who had been Captain of Westminster School could be important in some other phase of life, too!

Garrett Wesley returned just as Charles was beginning to get restless waiting for him.

"Well?" the Irishman said eagerly. "You look as if your decision pleased you."

"It does, sir," said Charles.

Garrett Wesley rubbed his hands together. His face beamed with a proud smile.

"You accept, of course!" he said. "Oh, you'll make a son a man can be proud of!"

"No, sir," said Charles quietly. "I thank you, and I am deeply grateful to you, but I must say 'No.' I do not wish to leave England for Ireland, or give up Oxford for Trinity College. I feel that my future is here."

The color all drained from Garrett Wesley's face.

"You *reject* my offer!" he cried. "You actually reject it, sir?"

"I do, Mr. Wesley," said Charles quietly. "I must."

The old Irishman was spluttering now, and Charles began to fear his kinsman would have a fit. Quickly, he rushed to the sideboard and poured a glass of port.

"Drink this, sir!" he cried.

Garrett Wesley drank, and gradually his splutterings subsided. By the time Dr. Freind came to see how they were getting on, the Irishman was in control of himself.

"He's turned me down, Headmaster!" Garrett Wesley said. "So I must look elsewhere for an heir."

The Headmaster looked at Charles. Charles met his glance frankly. Dr. Freind nodded.

"So Charles will go to Christ Church College," he said, "and there he will be a credit to us all."

Charles bowed his head. "I pray so, sir," he said. "I pray so."

8 Reunion in Epworth

That summer of 1726 Charles returned to Epworth for the first visit since he'd left home ten years before. Many changes had taken place in his absence. His father had become an old man, bowed down by the weight of family cares. His mother, weakened by the birth of her nineteenth child, was an invalid. Six of his sisters were still at home, too, typical examples of the "old maids," who were then so common in eighteenth century English households.

Charles was particularly saddened to see his mother forced to lie on the parlor sofa in idleness. He went in to her the first morning he was at home, wanting yet dreading to talk to her. She held out her hands to him, and he pressed them gently between his strong ones.

"Charles, Charles!" she cried, and there were tears in her eyes. "You've become a man!"

Charles smiled. "The years have been many, Mother," he said.

Susanna's lips trembled. "And the graves have multiplied in St. Andrew's Churchyard."

She was referring, Charles knew, to the ten graves of his brothers and sisters, the young Wesleys who had not been strong enough to endure sickness and lack of proper nourishment. He pressed her hands more tightly, hoping to comfort her. Apparently he succeeded, because her voice had a different quality when she spoke again.

"But you, Charles! You're off to Oxford. You've heard, of course, that your brother John has been elected a Fellow of Lincoln?"

"No, I had not heard!" cried Charles, and was ashamed of himself for the disappointment he felt at the news. Somehow, he had looked forward to Oxford as a place where he would be entirely without family supervision. Now, with John a Fellow, a tutor at Lincoln College, all that would be changed.

"How blessed I am with my three fine sons!" said Susanna.

Charles was even more ashamed of himself when she said that. He squared his shoulders, telling himself that thoughts were not deeds. He had *done* nothing to cause his mother pain.

"Perhaps John and I can get reacquainted when we are both at Oxford," he said. "You know, Mother, I saw him only once in all the years we were both in London. When I was allowed to move about a bit more in the city, he was already off to the University. Really, we are strangers."

Susanna nodded, but her face was calm. "The ties of blood are strong," she said. "We have not seen each other for ten years, either, but do you not feel at home with me?"

"I felt strange for a few moments last night," Charles said. "Everything in Epworth looks different to me, Mother. The church looks so tiny, the river so sluggish compared to the Thames."

"And I?" asked Susanna. A faint tinge of color crept into her pale cheeks, and she pushed back a strand of wispy gray hair.

"You are my mother," Charles said simply, hoping that would be enough.

"And John is your brother," Susanna said.

She waited a moment, long enough to let the thought settle in Charles's mind. "But you will not have to wait until you are both at Oxford to get reacquainted," she went on. "John is coming home for a visit before he takes up his position there."

Charles had several days to readjust to his surroundings before John arrived. It happened that he was in the village when the London coach rumbled up. He had ample time to get a good look at the one man who was set down at Epworth.

John Wesley was a short man, but that was no surprise to Charles, who was rather short himself. John was small, though, and pale and thin, with sharp features and straight lusterless hair. *He'd* never be likened to one of the baroque *putti*—cherubs—as Charles had been by one of his more flowery literary acquaintances!

Feeling curiously heartened by this vain thought, Charles waved his hat.

"Brother John!" he called, and hurried forward.

"Brother Charles?" said John, a faint question in his voice. "Why, of course. Brother Charles!"

They embraced each other, then drew apart to look into each other's eyes.

"The years have been good to you, Brother Charles," John said, stooping to lift his shabby little trunk.

"Here, let's carry it between us," said Charles. "Well," he added, belatedly acknowledging John's comment, "you have done very well, yourself, Brother John."

John looked at him, and Charles saw an almost steely glint in his gray eyes.

"I have not done nearly well enough," John said. "I have not lived up to the challenge you threw me, all those long years ago, Brother Charles."

Charles frowned. "Challenge *I* threw you? When? I've only seen you once in the past ten years, and then we spent our time on our knees in St. Paul's Cathedral, because you believed you needed to be forgiven for something or other you'd done. There wasn't time for me to challenge you!"

"I suppose you wouldn't remember," John said. "It was

just before I left Epworth for Charterhouse School. You teased me about the way Father called me 'a brand plucked from the burning.' "

Charles's frown deepened. "But that wasn't a *challenge*."

"What you said next was. 'You'll have to lead a saintly life, Brother John,' you said, 'to prove to the Lord you were worth saving!' "

Charles felt shocked at the words he was reported as having spoken. "That was a fine way to say 'goodbye!' "

John smiled, and Charles noticed how much more attractive his face was when its expression of gloom was lifted.

"It was the thoughtless expression of a little boy," John said, "but it has given a pattern to my life. It was seared into my mind as if by a real burning brand."

They walked on in silence for a few moments, John's last words hanging between them almost as tangibly as the trunk. When finally they reached the flagstone path that led up to the Rectory, John spoke again.

"I'm not a saint, Brother Charles. I like to eat rich foods, so I punish myself by fasting. I like to joke and dance with pretty girls, so I try to avoid their company."

John's words made Charles want to laugh, but he knew they were spoken in all seriousness, so he controlled himself. "That kind of conduct seems saintly to me," he said.

John shook his head, but said no more, because the door to the Rectory flew open and the Wesley girls came out all together. Behind them was the old Rector, supporting the frail Susanna with one trembling arm.

"The Prodigal Son returns!" Charles murmured.

John had either not heard him or chose to ignore the Biblical implication of Charles's remark.

Twittering like a flock of birds, the sisters took the small trunk from their brothers. John hurried forward to embrace both his parents and to urge them back to the security of their parlor.

Later, when they had all calmed down a little, John said suddenly, "I see the charred stick still hangs above the door."

The Rector nodded.

"Does anyone ever notice it any more?" John asked.

Susanna looked shocked at his words. "Of course!" she said. "It helps me through many a moment of discouragement. It reminds me that the Lord saved you, John, when we were sure no help was possible."

Susanna's words made John look at Charles, and Charles seemed to hear again John's cry of dissatisfaction with himself. Neither of them said anything, though, and after a fractional pause Susanna continued speaking.

"As if it were yesterday, I can see your father, counting over the members of our household. In front of us, the Rectory was a mass of orange flames. 'We cannot save it!' cried the men who had been fighting the fire. Your father had finished counting, then, and he answered—"

"Let the house go! I am rich enough!" cried the old Rector.

His words rang out with a strength Charles had never thought to hear from him again. They sent a shiver down Charles's back. Once again, it seemed he remembered being there, though he knew he was only remembering all the times he had heard the story before.

Charles looked at John, curious to see the way the reliving of that fearful time was affecting him. John was sitting with his head bowed and his hands in prayer position.

Charles felt a surge of pity for this brother, from whom so much was expected. How dreadful it would be to feel impelled always to criticize and justify one's own actions!

"I'm glad," Charles thought, "I'm so glad that I'm not John!"

9 Freedom with a Capital F

Charles entered Oxford, determined not to let the presence of his brother John rule his life in any way. For the first time ever, he was free with a capital F, and he wanted to kick up his heels and enjoy himself.

The University, in this period of the second King George, was certainly not burdened by any rules that would dampen Charles's desires. In common with England as a whole, it was suffering from a period of exhaustion. Few of the professors—dons, as they were called at Oxford—ever lectured. If they did, they didn't care whether students listened to them or not. Examinations were a farce: any answer would do. Those students who wished to study might, of course, since the splendid libraries were always available, but they were really on their own if they did.

After the strict discipline of Westminster School, Oxford seemed like a big playground to Charles. It was a regular theater for him to act in exactly as he saw fit. Since he was an attractive young man who enjoyed company, he had no trouble at all gathering a group of other gay blades around him.

"The Group," as Charles called himself and his friends, did everything together. They took the Oxford punts and went boating on the river. They attended cock fights and bear-baiting. They sat long hours in the inns of the town, drinking nut-brown ale and talking, talking, talking. They also attended every play that was presented in Oxford, and later acted out the parts to amuse themselves all over again.

Other things besides his good looks and attractive manners made Charles the life of the party. His talent for making up verse, which had been encouraged by Vincent Bourne at Westminster School, was greatly admired. So, too, was his ability to play the German flute.

Indeed, Charles was soon the talk of Oxford, and John naturally heard about his brother's activities. John came to visit Charles in his chambers one day and luckily found him at home.

"Welcome, Brother John!" Charles cried, sweeping a batch of playbills from a chair by the fire so that John could sit down.

"Do you indeed welcome me, Brother Charles?" asked John, sitting down but not sitting comfortably back. "I rather think you've been avoiding me."

Charles shrugged. "I've been busy."

"So I have heard," said John.

Something in the tone of John's voice made Charles feel defensive. "I've done nothing wrong!"

"Nothing sinful, perhaps," said John, "unless to waste your talents is sinful. I think that, at the very least, is shameful."

Charles's eyes flashed. "I'm not doing anything I'm ashamed of!"

"Aren't you?" John flipped over some of the playbills with the toe of his boot. "Do you think you were given a scholarship in order that you might attend every dramatic production that is staged in the city? That you might tootle your flute at evening musicales?"

"It's all a part of education," Charles insisted.

"But not the part to which you should give the lion's share of your time," said John.

Charles got up from his chair and began to pace restlessly up and down the room. He brushed against his black undergraduate's gown, causing it to swing as if embodied with life. He took up his scholar's hat and set it rakishly on his head.

"See!" he said to John. "I'm a scholar of Christ Church College!"

John looked more disapproving than ever. "You have that gown by the grace of my good friend, the Vicar of Broadway. It belongs to his son, Robin Griffiths, who died while still at Oxford."

"I know that—" said Charles.

"Robin Griffiths was a true scholar," said John. "I wonder what the vicar would think of *you,* Brother Charles."

"Perhaps that he wishes Robin had had some gaiety before he died!" cried Charles, flinging himself down in his chair again and staring defiantly at John. "You told me yourself last summer that you like to eat good food and dance and joke!"

"That's true," said John, "but I think I am breaking myself of those fleshly desires."

"But you've had them!" said Charles. "Would you deny me them without a trial? Would you have me become a saint all at once, just because you feel compelled to be one? Well, I'm not ready to be a saint quite yet, Brother John, and I'm not sure I *ever* want to be!"

John's face always pale, was blotched with red now. His gray eyes looked almost black, so deeply was he feeling the blow of Charles's words. Charles felt instant pity for this brother whom he had hurt so unnecessarily, and he put out his hand as if to soothe away the pain.

John shook his head as if to clear it and rose unsteadily to his feet. "I must go back to my college now," he said, "for I have some students who need me."

Charles showed him to the door. "I'm sorry, Brother John. I'm truly sorry," he said, though he wasn't sure exactly what he was sorry about.

John's words had made some impression on him, though, and in the days that followed he did go occasionally to the Bodleian Library to read. He even turned down a few invitations to go partying, in favor of finishing a treatise he had begun to study.

Sam came to see him once shortly after John's visit. Charles welcomed him eagerly, for he knew that this brother, at least, would not take him to task for enjoyment of innocent pleasure. After all, it was Sam who had introduced him to the literary world, to the men who wrote the novels he liked to read and the plays he liked to see performed.

"It's good to see you Brother Samuel!" Charles cried.

Sam looked around Charles's rooms with a tolerant gaze. Clothes were strewn everywhere. The hearth was full of ashes, and dust was thick on floor and furniture.

"In revolt against order, I see!" said Sam.

Charles tossed his head. "I suppose it could do with a good sweeping, if I had a brush-broom handy, as I always did in my Westminster cubicle."

"Don't you have a char?" asked Sam. "A woman to clean? I always did, when I was at Oxford."

"Oh, I have her when things get too much for me," said Charles, "but she costs money and I haven't any to throw away." He drew a chair forward for Sam. "But sit down, do! I have so much to show you!"

When Sam was comfortably settled, Charles brought out page after page of poetry he had written. He wrote about anthing and everything that took his fancy. He wrote about the ivy that climbed up all the Oxford walls, about the swans that glided on the river. He described what he saw on his long rambling walks around the University town, what he heard in the medley of sounds surrounding him in the theaters and inns.

"Do you like them?" he asked eagerly, when Sam had had time to read several.

Sam looked back over the verses he had read.

"You picture everything very clearly," he said. "I can see that old mill stream, and the wheel that turns at the mill. I can hear the doves that hide beneath the eaves at the Pig and Whistle Inn—"

"Yes?" prompted Charles, his eyes glowing.

"But I can't *feel* anything, Brother Charles. You don't *make* me feel."

Charles's heart seemed to drop into the toes of his boots.

"But poetry is no good without feeling!" he cried. He grabbed the pages from Samuel's lap and leafed through them rapidly. He read aloud a line or two here and there. "Don't *they* make you feel anything?" he asked.

Samuel shook his head.

"Then I might just as well tear the whole batch up!" cried Charles, and twisted his hands as if to rip the pages.

Samuel took the poems away from him.

"Don't do that!" he said. "Put them away. Someday you may remember how you felt when you saw the scenes you picture. Then you can go back and blow life into them."

Charles shuffled the pages into a neat pile. Then he went to his clothes press and found a box to put them in. While Samuel watched, he placed the box at the very back of the wardrobe.

"There," he said.

Then he sat down opposite Sam again, and both brothers stared thoughtfully into the cold, ash-strewn fireplace.

"Why is there no feeling in my poetry, Brother Samuel?" Charles said at last. "How could I write poetry without it?"

Sam pressed the tips of his fingers together, a sure sign to Charles that his brother was weighing his words.

"I think I know why and how," Sam said at last, "but you are not going to like what I tell you."

Charles laughed mirthlessly. "Anything would be mild, after the dressingdown I got from Brother John."

"Brother John and I go about things differently," said Sam, "but it may be we reach the same conclusion."

"Well?" asked Charles, feeling a shiver run down his spine.

"It is very simple," said Sam. "You are leaving God out of your life, Brother Charles."

Charles flinched, as if Sam had struck him.

"Is that what Brother John told you?" asked Sam.

Charles brushed a hand across his eyes, for moisture was gathering there.

"I think it may be," he whispered. "I think it probably is."

10 The Narrow Gate

"You are leaving God out of your life."

Those words from Samuel had gone straight to Charles's heart, causing him pain that was almost physical in its intensity. When he had recovered a little from the anguish, he set himself down soberly to consider the accusation.

Was he, in fact, only paying lip service to the Lord? He said his prayers night and morning. He attended both Matins and Evensong in the University Church, and very few of the other students could boast of such loyalty!

Charles flushed. Had he, recently Captain of Westminster School, actually sunk so low that he had to compare himself to other students to justify his actions? More to the point, would he have been elected Captain of Westminster at all, if he had acted as irresponsibly there as he had at Oxford?

Quite overcome by the questions he asked himself, Charles sank to his knees. He remembered how often his mother had said, "When you are in trouble, ask the Lord to help you." Now, for the first time since he had come to Oxford, words of pleading tumbled from his lips.

"Visit this soul of mine; pierce the gloom of my grief!" he cried.

Afterwards, he felt so much better that he rushed for pen and ink to write down the words that had burst from his heart.

"Maybe someday they will help others," Charles said to

himself, excited at the renewal of his feeling that rereading the words inspired. "Maybe this is the kind of verse I was meant to write!"

In his extremity of emotion, Charles rushed down the stairs, knowing only that he wanted to see John. He ran through the streets of Oxford, oblivious to the calls of friends. His heart pounded as he beat on John's door.

"Brother John! Brother John! Let me in!" he cried.

He heard slow footsteps approaching the door. Soon it swung back, and John stood there, looking dazedly at him.

"Were you asleep?" asked Charles. He waved his new verse in the air. "No matter! You'll wake up and shout when you hear this, Brother John. Listen!"

Before he could start to read, though, John spoke up. "Our father is ill, Brother Charles. I am leaving by the next coach for Epworth. I shall preach in Father's place until he is well again."

The light of excitement died from Charles's eyes. "You?" he asked numbly.

"I am an ordained minister, Brother Charles. Had you forgotten?"

Charles had, but that wasn't of any importance now. "How ill is Father? Should I go with you?"

"No!" said John. "The best thing you can do for him, for the family, is stay here and attend faithfully to your own business."

"Which is to apply myself diligently to my studies," said Charles. "Well, you may assure Father that I will do just that."

"He does not know you have ever failed to do so," said John, "and he won't hear it from me. Now, I really must go, Brother Charles. Will you walk with me to the coaching inn? Perhaps on the way you can tell me what you came to say."

Charles looked at the paper he had waved so proudly

a few minutes ago. It was crumpled, now, for his hand had clenched it when he heard John's sad news.

"It's of no importance now, Brother John," he said, but he smoothed the paper and folded it. "Shall we get started?"

He picked up a pile of books John had prepared to take with him and, when John wasn't looking, slipped the page inside one of them. Perhaps, he thought, when John finds it, he'll know he need not completely despair of me.

Charles saw John safely inside the coach. His brother had had to wrestle with his conscience, Charles was sure, to justify traveling in velvet luxury. No doubt he had felt it would not do to arrive in Epworth atop the coach, not when he must preserve a dignified appearance to reassure the people of his father's parish that he was equal to the job!

"Goodbye, Brother John," Charles said, when the coachman took his place and picked up the reins. "Tell our mother my heart goes out to her!"

"Pray for our father, Brother Charles," John said.

"Stand back!" cried the coachman.

Charles closed the coach door with a snap, noticing that the leather was rubbed and worn for many years of service. He watched the four-horse team as it trotted down the High Street and turned north on Cornmarket. Then, instead of following it, he turned down Alfred Street to where Blue Boar Street and Bear Lane met.

At the Blue Boar Inn, he was hailed by a group of merry friends.

"Well met!" one of them cried. "Sit down, friend Charles. We're planning a rousing night, and you and your flute are just what we need to cap it!"

"Yes!" cried another. "Your flute and your ballad-singing voice will be the crowning touch, Charles Wesley."

"Hear, hear!" cried the other young men, clinking their mugs together. "Hear, hear!"

A young serving girl, neat in mob cap and apron, was

standing at Charles's side. She bodded a curtsy and said, "What will you have, sir?"

Charles's blue eyes looked at her blankly for a moment. Then, realizing he was hungry, he said, "Two mutton chops and some greens, Molly, if you please."

He sat down at the table where his friends made room for him. The air was thick with smoke and the smell of people too closely packed together. After his brisk walk in the fresh air, Charles found this unpleasant. He thought of John, rolling away north toward Banbury now across the open fields, and his breathing became labored.

"What's amiss, Charles?" asked the young man next to him.

"With me, nothing," Charles answered through scarcely open lips. "But I have just learned that my father is very ill, and I am somewhat depressed in spirit."

His friend started to speak again, but Charles stopped him. "Say nothing about it, I beg of you. I will eat, because I must, but then I shall go back to my rooms."

The friend nodded. "I'll make your excuses," he said, "and keep the lads from bothering you."

When his food came, Charles ate quickly. Then he arose and said a general "Goodbye."

A clamor at once broke from his friends, but the young man who had been sitting next to Charles said: "Let him go!" In their surprise, they were silenced.

Charles walked away from the Blue Boar Inn and down St. Aldate's to his college. He went at once to the library there and stayed until far into the night.

Charles had thought it would be a relief to be rid of the presence of John at Oxford. Odly enough, though, as soon as he fully realized John was nowhere around to hear and disapprove of his actions, he missed his brother. He began to look at the gay parties and noisy talk sessions with the sort of aloofness John must have had toward them. The minute he could do that, he realized how very unworthy that sort of pastime was, after all.

He did not stop these diversions all at once, but on the way home from a musicale one night something John had said recurred to him. "Narrow is the gate and hard is the way that leads to life." Charles puzzled over that quotation, knowing it was only half of the story, yet unable to think of the other part.

As soon as he was back in his rooms once more, he took up the Bible he had neglected so long. When he felt the familiar leather binding and saw the worn purple ribbon place-mark, he felt a curious warmth all through his body.

"Narrow is the gate," he said aloud. The words would be found in one of the Gospels, of that he was sure, but he could not remember in which.

He carried his candle over to the table beside his fire-side chair. Sitting down, he began to leaf through the New Testament, starting with the Book of Matthew. Familiar words stared up at him—the Beatitudes, the Lord's Prayer—and suddenly he knew just where he would find the words he was seeking, and indeed what the words that followed were.

Eagerly, he turned to Matthew 7:13 and his pointing finger followed the lines:

> Enter by the narrow gate; for the gate is wide and the way is easy that leads to destruction, and those who enter by it are many. For the gate is narrow and the way is hard that leads to life, and those who find it are few.

Not long after that moment of rediscovery of the Bible, Charles found himself writing a letter to John such as he had never expected to write. In it, he said how much he missed John, and how sorry he was for anything he had said or done that hurt:

> There is no one person I would so willingly have to be the instrument of good to me as you. It is through your means I firmly believe that God will accomplish what He hath begun in me.

He went on to offer practical proof of his willingness to be guided by John, finishing on a wondering note that showed he himself did not quite know why he had had a change of heart:

> It is owing in great measure to somebody's prayers that I am come to think as I do; for I cannot tell myself how or when I first awoke out of my lethargy, only that it was not long after you went away.

John, of course, replied to his brother. The variety of religion John practiced was largely a matter for himself alone. Therefore, his directions to Charles were for the same type of lonely observance:

> Apply yourself diligently to all tasks.
> Adopt a plan of self-examination.
> Pray with fervor.

Charles, as eager now to heed his brother's suggestions as he formerly was to reject them, tried to do as John said. He and John were temperamentally very different, though, and Charles found that he could not solve his problems alone or in silence. Therefore, he began to look around for other young men who seemed to think as he now did.

As he had been able to find a group to follow him in frivolity, so now he easily found a group willing to be serious with him. Before long, Charles was once again the talk of Oxford, this time as the leader of a band of Methodists.

11 The Holy Club

The jeering students who called Charles and his followers "Methodists" did not invent the name. For at least one hundred years, it had been a common term of ridicule in church disputes. As the undergraduates used it, though, it referred to the way of life the newly serious young men had undertaken.

Charles had persuaded his new "group" to look with him at the method of study prescribed by the statutes of the University. To their amazement, they discovered that the rules were very strict indeed, particularly those that related to attendance at church services.

"Have you the courage," Charles said, "to carry them out to the letter? Our fathers and grandfathers did. Are we less strong than they?"

"No!" cried William Morgan, a fellow student at Christ Church College.

"Of course not!" shouted Richard Kirkham, a Merton College scholar.

"Then," said Charles, "I have an idea that I think will help us. Let us form a society with rules and regulations that will help us to be strong and to strengthen each other."

There was method in Charles's suggestion, because he knew that the idea of a club would be appealing. Clubs were very popular in England in the eighteenth century, and there was one for every conceivable interest. Why not for a group interested in taking education seriously?

"A praiseworthy idea!" Richard Kirkham said.

"And to show our detractors we are not bothered by name-calling, let us call ourselves the Methodist Club," proposed Charles.

They drew up a set of regulations at once. They agreed, among other things:

1. To spend three or four evenings a week together.
2. To read over in company those portions of the classics which they had already read in private.
3. To read on Sunday evenings some book of Divinity.

Like so many other religious enthusiasts, the Methodists began to overdo the outward observance of their belief. They took to attending the Sacrament of the Lord's Supper four times more often than the University rules suggested. They were loud in their goodness and self-righteousness and soon attracted the attention they all but asked for. The name-callers who had first dubbed them "Methodists" thought up a new term of derision—the Holy Clubbers.

This strict life into which Charles had entered of his own free will showed up quickly in his scholarship. By the time John returned to Oxford in 1729, Charles had been invited by the University to become a College tutor.

Charles called a special meeting of the Holy Club to introduce John to the other members. He asked John to lead them in prayer. John did, and prayed so powerfully that the group was moved to ask him to assume the leadership in place of Charles.

John, of course, had been leading a methodical life for years, but when he had left for Epworth, Charles had resisted every effort John had made to get Charles to follow such a regime.

"You are sure, Brother Charles," John said to Charles privately now, "that you really wish me to replace you? I warn you, what I will expect of you will not be easy."

Charles knew John must be remembering his defiant cry of two years before: "What, would you have me be a saint all at once?"

"Yes," he said, "I do wish it."

"So be it," said John, turning back to the other members of the group. "It is my firm conviction," he said, "that if we are to follow Christ, we must discipline ourselves every moment."

He proceeded to draw up for them a far more exacting set of rules than they had had before. He taught them his methodical ways of study and of work. He worked out exactly how much sleep was necessary to each one and exactly how much time had to be wasted in eating. In short, he imposed such a tight discipline on their every move that all joy and spontaniety were removed from their lives.

Taking a short vacation in the summer of 1729, Charles went to London to visit his brother Sam at Westminster. Samuel, naturally overjoyed to see this young brother to whom he had been practically a father for so many years, had planned several gay affairs to entertain him. Charles, as befitted his behavior as a guest, attended these affairs but took no interest in them. Samuel was amazed and disturbed.

"You have become so dull and spiritless, Brother Charles," Sam complained. "If I did not have the eyes to see you with, I would think you were Brother John and not Brother Charles at all!"

"I consider that a compliment, Brother Samuel," said Charles. "To be like our brother John is the present goal of my life!"

"But why?" cried Sam, disappointment ringing in his question. "You, always such a wit, such an addition to every gathering! Why let Brother John sap all the enjoyment of life from you?"

For a moment, Charles was aroused. "He that has begun to live by rule has gone a great way toward the perfection of his life!" he cried.

"What's that?" demanded Samuel. "The Gospel according to Brother John? It strikes me as a wholly selfish way of living. Why, the most perfect man who ever lived was Jesus. But He thought always of others before Himself. Where have you left room for social consciousness in your pattern for existence, Brother Charles?"

"I hope to lead others to follow the methodical life, as John has led me," Charles said.

Samuel looked as if he would burst into tears. Charles, remembering how close he and Sam had been once, wished he could say something reassuring to his older brother.

"Brother Samuel," he said, "when you came to see me at Oxford, you told me I was leaving God out of my life. It was that accusation of yours that started me on the road I am now traveling!"

Sam stared at Charles. "I never meant to direct you on such a narrow path," he said.

Charles's blue eyes suddenly sparkled. "Ah, but why not?" he cried. "Narrow is the gate that leads to life, Brother Samuel!"

Sam shook his head. "You can find words in the Bible to apply to any situation. What is important is the *way* you apply them!"

Charles started to retort, but Samuel stopped him.

"Have you written any poetry lately, Brother Charles?" he asked. "I would be interested to see whether the fault I found with the last I saw has been corrected."

"I have written some prayers," Charles said. "Some verses which, set to music, we sing at our meetings."

"Meetings?" asked Samuel.

"Why, yes!" said Charles, and for a moment a smile trembled at the corner of his lips. "They call us the 'Holy

Club' at Oxford, because we attend church together on every possible occasion."

"It doesn't sound like a term of affection," said Samuel.

"It isn't," said Charles. "They don't understand how a group of young men can want to lead a devout and holy life, even while attending a secular college."

"Perhaps," suggested Samuel, "they would feel more affection for you if you thought of them occasionally instead of yourselves."

"Of them?" repeated Charles. "They don't want us to think of them!"

"Don't they?" asked Sam. "Perhaps instead of 'them' I should say 'other people.' "

He yawned and stretched deliberately, as if to indicate that their conversation had gone on long enough. "Sleep on that thought, Brother Charles," he suggested, "and we'll talk again tomorrow before you leave."

The next day, Samuel gave a book to Charles. "Here," he said, "this is currently the talk of London."

It was a long time since Charles has held any book in his hands except scholarly tomes or the Bible. He took Sam's offering unwillingly. When he read the title, though, his face cleared.

"*Serious Call to a Devout and Holy Life,* by William Law," he said aloud. He looked at Samuel wonderingly. "After our conversation of last night, this is hardly the kind of book I would have expected *you* to give *me!*"

He opened the book and read the beginning sentence. " 'Devotion signifies a life given or devoted to God.' Why, Brother Samuel, this is just the sort of book my friends and I should have!" he cried.

Sam smiled. "Curiously enough, I agree," he said.

On that note, the brothers parted.

12 Further Adventures of the Holy Club

Charles mounted to the roof of the London-Oxford coach. He was relieved to see that the benches had sides, because that meant there was less danger of his being thrown off balance. He settled himself as comfortably as possible, bracing his feet against his traveling bag. Then, paying no attention to his fellow travelers, he took Samuel's gift book out of his pocket and began to read.

He had expected, and even hoped, that the book would be dull. On the contrary, though, he found it as interesting as it was instructive. There were twenty-four chapters, all of them expanding and illustrating the opening sentence he had read aloud to Samuel: "Devotion signifies a life given or devoted to God." In each chapter Law used a different type of personality to illustrate his theme.

"Why," said Charles to himself, "this William Law is as good at character sketches as Joseph Addison himself! I can see each of the people—the mother, the parson, the merchant—as clearly as I can see these people atop the coach with me!"

Thinking that, he took his first real look at the other top-coach riders. He found himself wondering about them, and wishing he had the time to talk to them.

He scolded himself, however, for even considering such an unmethodical diversion, and gave his full attention to the book once more. With satisfaction, he noted that William Law, too, favored a rigid time schedule, with every moment of every day planned for.

Then it was that Charles discovered where Law's methods and Wesley's methods differed. He knew at once why Samuel had smiled, and why he had agreed with Charles that Law's book was just what he and his Holy Club friends needed.

The difference was all important. Whereas John emphasized that every moment ought to be directed toward helping *oneself* toward salvation, William Law emphasized the need for helping *others* achieve it. Law, in fact, believed that each day should start with a charitable act, and thus set a pattern for the hours that followed.

Charles could scarcely wait to get to Oxford and to set his friends to reading the *Serious Call*. Fortunately, it was Sunday evening, and the Methodists would be meeting in John's rooms. This book would be perfect as the prescribed "book of Divinity" to read aloud to the group!

The other Methodists were just as excited by William Law's book as Charles was. It succeeded, where Samuel never could have, in persuading John and Charles and their followers to give up some of their self-absorption and to start applying some of their zeal outside their own little circle.

Before long, in fact, they were spending all their spare time in seeking out the needy and making the sick as comfortable as their means allowed. They urged church attendance; they even taught illiterates to read, using, as Susanna had, the Bible as their primer.

The jails of the eighteenth century were terrible places. The jailer was the lord and master of his prison, and the fate of his captives was entirely in his hands. If the prisoner had money to pay for them, he received bedding, food, and water. If he did not, he might lie on the cold, wet floor and die of starvation, for all the jailer cared.

The plight of the prisoner was beginning to get some attention in the last years of the third decade, mainly because the friend of a Member of Parliament had died in Fleet Prison from hunger and neglect. The tragedy was particularly sad because the man, Cassel, had been imprisoned on a false charge.

The M.P., James Oglethorpe, had been out of the country and did not know of his friend's situation until too late to help him. Cassel did not die in vain, though, because his death moved Oglethorpe to ask the House of Commons for an official investigation into the state of the prisons of England. A committee was formed for just such a purpose, with Oglethorpe himself as chairman.

The Committee discovered that a sentence to jail was, indeed, a sentence to death. Once the prison gates clanged behind a man, he was a forgotten soul, unless someone on the outside cared enough to remember him.

The findings of the Committee aroused certain people to start working towards prison reform, but it was a long, uphill fight. It was, in fact, just the sort of crusade young zealots were looking for.

One day in 1730, William Morgan came to a meeting of the Holy Club all fired with enthusiasm.

"I went to the Castle Prison today," he cried, "and I talked with some of the prisoners. Poor souls, they were so glad to talk to someone. I prayed with them, and they looked at me as if I were the good Lord Himself! I think we Methodists should make a special point of visiting the jails!"

Morgan's enthusiasm quite stirred the other club members. They determined to make room for twice-weekly prison visitation in their schedules.

The result was that the Methodists were more than ever the cause of amazement to their fellows at Oxford. The average undergraduate could not understand why anyone wanted to expose himself to the filth and disease-laden air of any prison. The citizens of the city of Oxford agreed with the students. Moreover, they thought the Wesleys and their followers were meddling in an area that was none of their business.

At first, the objectors contented themselves with calling the Methodists mocking names. Later, though, when they saw their words had no effect, they took to throwing stones, mud, and rotten vegetables.

Once when Charles came out of the Castle Prison, he was hit squarely in the face by a tomato. He stood there, with the red juice running down his face like blood and staining his black gown. He looked at his tormentors, his blue eyes clear and unwavering, and soon the crowd turned and went away.

This show of bravery on Charles's part attracted certain other well-meaning young men to him. Gradually, the little band of Methodists acquired new recruits, among them a student named George Whitefield.

Whitefield's background was as different as could be from the Wesleys'. His mother, a widow, ran the Bell Inn at Gloucester. At the age of five, when Charles Wesley was learning his alphabet at his mother's knee, George Whitefield was already a "pot boy," drawing beer and pouring gin for his mother's customers.

Like Charles, though, George Whitefield loved plays and playacting. He saved every tip a customer gave him, and when he had enough money for a ticket, he'd find his way to the local theater. Like Charles, too, George had a fine singing voice, and used it on every occasion.

He was at Oxford in the position of serving-boy at Pembroke College, his fees paid in return for services rendered to certain rich lordings. However, he, too, had read William Law's *Serious Call,* and had ordered his own days with a method that worked well for him.

"I have longed to meet you," he told Charles, when

finally he screwed up the courage to speak to the younger Wesley. "For almost a year I have watched you go about your business of mercy, wishing I were brave enough and good enough to join you."

"Are we so formidable?" asked Charles.

George Whitefield shook his head. "Not you, but what you stood for. I did not think I was brave enough to stand the kind of treatment you and the others receive."

"What changed your mind?" asked Charles.

"When I saw the crowd turn away as if whipped by merely a glance from you, I knew I needed you," Whitefield said simply. "My soul is athirst for someone to lift up my hands when they hang down, and strengthen my feeble knees. I have never known anyone who could before."

Charles felt very humble when he heard George Whitefield's needs. He himself had always had someone. First, there was his mother, Susanna. Next, there was his brother, Samuel. Now he had John.

"I will introduce you to my brother John," Charles told George Whitefield. "He is more experienced than I am. Why, he is almost a saint!"

The young Methodists' other recruits were from various colleges—John Gambold of Christ Church, John Clayton of Brasenose, and Benjamin Ingham of Queen's College. They all found rigid adherence to forms and ceremonies to their liking, and they were willing to accept the Bible as an infallible guide for life.

For six years, this little group of Methodists lived the lives of martyrs—eating too little, sleeping too little, driving themselves too hard. William Morgan, who had first suggested the prison visitations, spent so much time in the damp dungeons that he acquired "lung fever"—tuberculosis. John was the victim of chronic stomach trouble. Charles, too, was ill very often, but he forced himself to maintain as rigid a schedule as ever.

Often, Charles was so sick he longed to lie down and die. Since, however, he believed that life was only a training ground for the life everlasting, he felt he had to pile up credits on earth, as many as possible.

In the summer of 1735, both Charles and John were summoned to Epworth. The Reverend Samuel was dying, and he wanted to see all his children once more.

Charles spent a long time alone with him one afternoon. They had not been alone with each other like this for years, not since Charles had sat with the Rector to learn Greek and Latin. Memory of those days lay in the eyes of father and son as they looked at each other.

Quickly, because there was so much to say, Charles spoke of his years at Westminster, of his years at Oxford, and of the Holy Club. The Rector listened quietly until Charles started to tell of the work the young Methodists were doing. Then the old man held up his hand to stop Charles's flow of words.

"I have to tell you what your mother said, when both your letters and John's became increasingly full of the work you and your friends were doing," the Reverend Samuel said.

Charles felt a twinge of discomfort. "Mother does not approve?" he asked.

"In principle, yes, of course," said the Rector, "but she thinks there is something lacking in the way you strive self-centeredly for salvation."

"What did Mother say?" Charles asked then.

" 'I wish,' she said, 'that they would talk less of themselves and more of God.' "

Charles repeated his mother's words to himself, and he felt bruised all over. They were just a variation of what Samuel had said years before: "You are leaving God out of your life."

Like a little child, he clasped his father's hand. "Father," he said, "tell me what to do!"

The Rector started to reply, but suddenly his face contorted, and he gripped Charles's hand as if it were a lifeline. He gasped, and beads of perspiration broke out on his forehead.

Charles, who had found the words to comfort prisoners condemned to die, could think of nothing to say to his father. He took a cloth and with his free hand gently wiped the Rector's face.

Gradually, the old man relaxed his hold and soon he was able to smile.

"Your face is as white as an altar cloth," he said to Charles. "I am sorry I frightened you."

"Oh, Father!" cried Charles, overcome by the fact that at such a time his father could think of *him*. "I wish I had as clear a faith as you and Mother do! Why don't I? Where have I lost my way?"

The Rector looked at him with eyes that were serene and clear. "My faith is simple, my Charles," he said. "I believe in God."

"Even when he makes you suffer so?" asked Charles.

"Especially then," said his father. "God chastens me with strong pain, even as His Son suffered. I praise Him for it. I love Him for it!"

Charles shook his head, not understanding.

The old man laid his hand on the shaking head. "Be steady, Charles. Be steady. The Christian faith will revive in men's hearts. It will revive in *your* heart."

He lay back on his pillows, and closed his eyes.

That evening he died.

13 A Piece of Thistledown

Shortly after Charles and John had returned to Oxford, the Holy Club broke up. One by one, their education completed, the other members left the University to take up their adult lives.

Charles envied them, because they knew what they wanted to do. He himself not only did not know what he wanted—he had no idea what he was fitted to do. His last talk with his father had raised so many doubts in his mind that he felt unworthy even to keep on with his prison visiting. Who was he to comfort the doomed, when he felt so lost himself?

He and John lingered on at Oxford through the summer months, following the same routines they had followed for the past six years. All about them, though, they saw changes in the social scene. In particular, they were aware of the changing character of the prisons.

The Parliamentary investigation led by James Oglethorpe had begun to have a marked effect. The M.P.'s had staged a successful campaign of fund-rasing, and the money went toward the release of debtors from jail. Formerly, such men had been forgotten once they were behind bars, unless a friend or personal benefactor provided the sum for their release. The Reverend Samuel Wesley himself had been twice in debtors' prison, so his sons knew the law was no respecter of persons.

The sudden release of so many homeless and penniless people presented England with another problem— what to do with them? James Oglethorpe felt compelled to provide an answer to that question. They could, he suggested, be sent to the New World, and there they could start life afresh. Where in the New World should they go? To a colony he himself would set up and govern—a place he would call "Georgia," in honor of England's king.

Oglethorpe envisioned Georgia as an Eden for all displaced or exiled persons, whether they were English or not. He wished to offer free passage and a home in the colony to anyone who felt the need of such a haven. Of course, he was not rich enough to carry such a financial burden on his own shoulders, so he sent out an appeal for help:

> We at once behold numbers of miserable men, destitute of habitations, and an uncultivated country destitute of inhabitants. May this critical coincidence be improved to the common advantage!

Oglethorpe was a persuasive man, and his appeal went to the hearts of the people. Everyone who could sent money, some great amounts, some tiny. In addition, large quantities of Bibles, books of piety, hornbooks, and household needs of all sorts were contributed.

John and Charles each sent more than they could afford. Their brother Samuel sent not only money but a pewter chalice and paten, too, so that the Lord's Supper might be suitably served in America. In addition, Samuel wrote a poem in the flowery style then common as a toast to the new colony and to its governor.

> How views the Mother Isle your little State!
> How aids the Senate! How the Nation loves!
> How George protects and Caroline approves!

Oglethorpe himself had sailed with the first batch of colonists in 1734. He had stayed with them until the foundations of the settlement were firmly laid. When he returned to England, he knew what he must have when he sailed to the New World again. His settlers were for the most part jailbirds, bankrupts, and outcasts. More than anything else, they needed spiritual guidance.

For help in selecting the right clergyman for the job, Oglethorpe went to his friend, Dr. John Burton of Corpus Christi College, Oxford. After much thought Dr. Burton, in turn, went to see John Wesley.

Charles and John were together when Dr. Burton came to call. They listened as he outlined what was needed.

"Your expenses would be met by the Society for the Propagation of the Gospel," said Dr. Burton, speaking of a recently founded group sponsored by the Church of England.

"And would I take Mr. Oglethorpe's place as shepherd of his black sheep?" asked John.

"That is his idea," said Dr. Burton. "But we of the S.P.G. would prefer to send you as a missionary to the American Indians."

John sat for some minutes, apparently deep in thought. Charles, glancing at him from time to time, felt a growing terror that John would accept. If John did, he—Charles—would be left behind without an anchor, without, indeed, anything to hold on to.

"I must think about your offer, Dr. Burton," John said. "I will give you my answer as soon as possible."

Dr. Burton sighed, but accepted John Wesley's decision. "Very well," he said, "but Governor Oglethorpe is anxious to complete his plans."

"I will not delay any longer than is absolutely necessary," said John.

As soon as the door had closed behind their visitor, John began to think aloud in a way that invited Charles's comments.

"I am reluctant to leave our widowed mother," he finished, "but I feel a call I cannot describe."

"Why don't you give our mother a chance to speak for herself in this matter?" Charles suggested, hoping his feeling of desperation did not sound in his voice.

John looked at him as if he had said something astounding. "Why, that's just what I shall do!" he cried. "She is in London with our sister Emily. I shall go at once!"

Feeling already as if John had left him, Charles groped for another lifeline.

"I'll go with you," he said. "It is a long time since I have seen Brother Samuel."

The brothers journeyed to London together, then parted company. Charles went on to Westminster, where Samuel welcomed him gladly.

"What brings you to London, Brother Charles?" Sam asked.

Charles told him about the Society for the Propagation of the Gospel, and of John's feeling that he should accept the challenge of going to the New World. He watched Samuel's face as he spoke, surprised to see that this older brother looked positively gleeful at the idea of John's departure.

"It will provide just the type of martyrdom our Brother John is looking for!" Samuel cried, when Charles had finished. "Add your urging to that of the S.P.G., Brother Charles!"

"But I will be lost without him," Charles said in such a low voice Samuel had to bend close to hear him.

"Nonsense!" cried Samuel. "You will be better off without him. Look at you—skin and bones instead of healthy flesh. You were meant to be a scholar, Brother Charles—not a saint!"

Samuel's words echoed in Charles's mind, reminding him of taunts he had flung at John in times past. "You'll have to lead a saintly life, Brother John, to prove to the Lord you were worth saving!" And again: "Would you have me become a saint all at once, Brother John?"

"I will not be the one to urge Brother John," Charles said, "but if he goes, I shall try to settle down at Oxford and be the scholar you think I am."

"And give up this driving yourself until life becomes a punishment," said Samuel.

John's interview with his mother was satisfactory from his point of view.

"Why, Brother Charles," he said, when they were on the way back to Oxford, "she said *of course* I should go. She said she had always favored missionary work and that you, at least, ought to remember that—"

Suddenly, Charles did remember. He was transported back through the years to the meetings Susanna held in the kitchen at Epworth. She had talked glowingly of the work Danish missionaries were doing in the East Indies. He even remembered asking: "What are missionaries, Mother?" and receiving the reply: "People sent out from their churches to preach and teach in foreign countries."

"Yes, I remember," said Charles.

John looked at him queerly. "Why didn't you tell me that before?"

"I didn't think of it," said Charles.

"Well," John said, "I have decided to go to America—but you are going with me!"

Charles's heart gave a great leap. "What gave you that idea?" he gasped. "I haven't been invited!"

"I shall see that you *are* invited," John said, a crusading light in his eyes. "I had a vision, Brother Charles—I saw the pointing finger of God. This is the opportunity He is giving us, to cut ourselves off from common ambitions and the easy rut of established things."

For just a minute, Charles thought of his brother Samuel, and his words: "It will provide just the type of martyrdom Brother John is looking for." Then, his joy that John wanted him overpowered Samuel's warnings.

"But what use can I be?" he cried.

"I'll talk to Dr. Burton tonight," John answered, "and tell him what I have decided. After that, it will be up to him."

John did talk to Dr. Burton, who set the necessary wheels in motion. As soon as that happened, Charles as well as John felt committed.

Charles wrote his brother Samuel before the details were known. Samuel answered him, urging him to reconsider, reminding him that he was not the type of which martyrs are made. By the time Samuel's answer came, however, Charles had agreed to go to America as secretary to Governor Oglethorpe.

This news, too, he wrote Sam. This time, Samuel's return letter admitted defeat, but issued another warning:

> Jack knew his strength and used it. His will was strong enough to bend you to go, though not with my consent. I freely own 'twas the will of Jack, but I am not convinced 'twas the will of God.

After that, events moved swiftly. Dr. Burton urged Charles to be ordained in the Church of England before he left, so that Governor Oglethorpe could take two clergymen to Georgia and thus double the spiritual guidance for the new colony.

"I am not good enough!" Charles protested, knowing the doubts that plagued him. "I have not faith enough to preach to others!"

"Nonsense," said John. "You can talk and charm the devil himself."

Charles still shrank from the thought of setting himself up as God's minister, but as he had so often, he gave in to John's urging.

"I'm like a piece of thistledown, blown by the winds of chance," he said to himself. "I seem not to have a will of my own any more."

14 Farewell to England

Early on the morning of Thursday, October 14, 1735, Charles and John approached Gravesend, England, where they were to embark for America. The coach horses trotted alongside the Thames River, went up and then down Windmill Hill and through irregular and narrow streets to the harbor.

Charles felt almost numb with the dread of leaving all that was familiar behind him. John had to prod him to get out of the coach when it reached the end of the line.

"Take a last look at Mother England," John said, almost jovially. "Who knows when—or if—we'll ever see her again!"

Almost like a puppet being jerked by strings, Charles did as John suggested. He saw the many boats that tugged at their moorings—the East Indiamen, with their cargoes of silks and spices; the ships-of-the-line, their guns gleaming in the sunshine; little fishing sloops; even barges, flying the king's pennant, ready to take visiting royalty by the water route to London.

He smelled the salt air, mixed with the odors of tar and rope, of coffee and cinnamon. He heard the sailors shouting to one another and the fish girls offering "oysters, hey, and cockles, fresh as the day itself!" Then he turned and looked away from the harbor scenes, looked back at the green hills that meant England to him, and his eyes filled with tears.

Someone clapped him on the shoulder. "Well met!" a familiar voice cried.

Blinking rapidly, Charles looked up. Through a mist, he saw Benjamin Ingham, one of the Holy Club members he had loved the best.

"Benjamin!' he cried. "How does it happen you are here?"

"What!" said Ingham. "Didn't John tell you? I am going to America with you!"

Charles clasped his friend's shoulders strongly with both hands. "Oh, I'm so glad, so glad!"

" 'Twill be like old times," Benjamin Ingham said.

"Not quite," said John, coming up in time to hear Ingham's last remark. He waved toward the *Simmonds,* the wooden sailing ship that was to be their residence for many months. "Instead of the whole city of Oxford, we'll have only that. She has a displacement of only two hundred and twenty tons and a company of one hundred and twenty-four souls to carry. Of course," he added, rubbing his palms together, "we should find it easy to carry the Gospel to them. There's only one main cabin, and all of us will share it!"

Charles and Benjamin exchanged glances, and Charles felt fortunate to have this dear friend along to share his new life.

The other passengers were English, except for twenty-six Moravian exiles from Austria. One of the Englishmen was Charles Delamotte, the son of a prosperous London merchant. He had come along for the thrill of adventure, but most of the other English-speaking people were as low morally and spiritually as any of the outcasts already settled in Georgia.

The former members of the Holy Club mapped out their shipboard days with the same methodical care they had exercised at Oxford. They arose at four o'clock each morning and prayed and read the Bible together privately for two hours. Charles, feeling the weight of his ordination, wrote sermons and religious verse between the hours of nine and twelve. Between dinner at one o'clock and public prayers at four, they conversed in religious terms with the other English-speaking passengers. In the hours not specifically accounted for, the brothers studied German, so they could talk with the Moravians.

Charles was very much attracted to these Austrian refugees who were fleeing from the persecution of the Archbishop of Salzburg. It was his first introduction to the Protestant mysticism of Germany, which they represented. The Moravians were gentle, humble, courageous people, who held their own religious services every day, in spite of opposition from some of the more unruly English passengers. Whenever possible with his schedule, Charles attended these services.

One phase of the services interested Charles in particular. These people sang songs themselves, a practice as yet unknown in Charles's experience. They sang with fervor and great feeling, so great that Charles's spirits felt uplifted just by listening to them.

"I wish," he said to Benjamin Ingham, "oh, I wish I had the faith they do!"

He did not say anything of the sort to John, though. John was too busy trying to interest his own flock in serious matters to bother with Charles's state of mind.

John, indeed, was not finding his task the easy one he had expected. Many people resented his insistence on holding public prayers twice a day. They did not wish to attend; but, as John had gleefully observed before the ship sailed, there was only one sitting room. Objectors were forced to be present, or else banish themselves to the cold and windy open deck.

At first, John had some success, or thought he did, with the young women among the passengers. They listened, wide-eyed, to his reading aloud from Law's *Serious Call* or Norris's *Christian Perfection.* They made a special point of engaging him in private "confessional" conversations.

John spoke with satisfaction to Charles about these women.

"Mrs. Hawkins, the wife of the doctor-to-be of the colony, is very eager to be instructed," he said. "So, too, is her friend, Mrs. Welch."

Charles, however, had been watching the overtures of the women to his brother. He had talked about them to Benjamin Ingham and to Charles Delamotte, who was a man of the world.

"They are flirting with you, Brother John," Charles warned. "You are a pleasant-appearing man, and young. They seek a pastime for the long shipboard hours."

"They seek to find a new meaning in life!" cried John.

Charles shook his head. "You are blinding yourself to the truth," he cried.

John would not give weight to Charles's warning, and he kept on trying to convince the women that the Gospel message was for *them*. Before long, they realized John cared nothing for them as women, indeed that it was their *souls* that interested him. They tried to get away from his insistent presence, for his religious conversations bored them exceedingly. John, however, seemed fired with further zeal by their withdrawing actions. He sought them out no matter where they went on shipboard

Finally, Mrs. Hawkins appealed to Charles.

"Mr. Wesley," she said, "tell your fanatical brother to leave us alone! He's like a millstone around our necks, and we want to be rid of him!"

Charles was shocked by the comparison of his saintly brother to a common millstone, however much he agreed that John would do better to leave them alone.

"You should not speak so of a man of God!" he cried.

The woman put her kerchief up to her nose, as if she smelled something bad.

"You keep him away from me, or I'll make you sorry you ever came on this trip to Georgia!"

Later, Charles noticed that both young women started to dog James Oglethorpe's footsteps instead of John's. The Governor treated them kindly, even familiarly.

Charles saw him kiss Mrs. Hawkins one time, and heard her flirtatious response. "Oh, la, Mr. Oglethorpe! Whatever would my husband say?"

No matter how open the women were in their pursuit of other men, however, John Wesley still believed he could convert them. Nothing Charles could say would convince him otherwise.

In this uneasy fashion, months passed on board the *Simmonds*. All through October, November, and December of 1735, wind and weather cooperated, and the ship proceeded steadily toward the New World.

Then one night in January, Charles awoke to something that sounded like cannon shots.

"Pirates!" was his first thought.

He leaped from his berth and started to dress. The ship lurched, and he lost his balance. He fell against his trunk, striking his knee so hard his whole leg ached from the blow.

"A bad storm," he said, on second thought.

The ship was alternately pitching and rolling now, and Charles could hear the slap! slap! of the great waves against the ship's sides.

He tried to make his way topside, but the gonig was very hard. The torches that ordinarily lighted the passages had been knocked from their sconces. The ship was in darkness.

The wooden timbers of the ship creaked alarmingly. Charles could not see anything, but he could hear the creaks like high violin squeaks amid the deep bass wailing of the wind.

Finally, he succeeded in groping his way up to the deck, only to be pushed back by a brawny seaman.

"Back with ye!" the seaman ordered. "It's a hurricane, and no one's safe on deck unless he be lashed to something."

Before the seaman got the hatch closed, Charles heard more creaks like gunshots.

"The sails are flying free!" the seaman cried. "They'll be all shreds and tatters, but there's no man can hold them in *this* blow!"

The candles in the main cabin were glowing by the time Charles got there. He could see the passengers in various stages of dress. Most of them were groaning, screaming or sobbing, but over in a corner the Moravians were on their knees in prayer.

John appeared in the doorway beside his brother. His teeth were chattering, and his face was as white as his shirt front.

"I must comfort the people," he said, looking at the wailing crowd. "How they huddle together, like sheep in a storm."

"They are frightened, Brother John," said Charles. "Nay, they are terrified!"

The ship rolled way over to one side. John was thrown against Charles. He clutched at his brother, and Charles felt desperation at this sign of John's lack of faith.

"Oh, Brother Charles!" whispered John in an agonized voice, "I am terrified, too! I am not ready to die!"

Charles thought of his father, of the peaceful expression on the old man's face, of his words: "I believe!"

"I am not ready to die, either," he said, and for a moment the brothers stood miserably clasped together.

Then the Moravians began to sing, and Charles felt a soothing warmth flow through his body as he listened to their calm, measured voices. When they were done, their Bishop's voice boomed out so all could hear him above the sound of the tempest.

"The way to God is as short by the sea as by soil!" he said.

A momentary hush followed the Bishop's proclamation, as if the wind and the waves had heard and approved. Then quite another voice was raised in unmistakable command.

"Lay off the prayers and lay on the work!" the captain shouted. "Man the pumps, every able-bodied man among you!"

For hours, everybody worked. Down in the hold, Charles and John with the other men stood in icy water to their knees. They pumped and pumped, and still the water level stayed the same.

In the face of this very real peril, John had nothing to say. The Moravian Bishop, though, kept praying as he worked.

"God, make our arms mighty. God, give us peace. If this be our hour, take us to thy bosom. Amen."

"Amen," whispered Charles.

He remembered his mother taking him to task for saying "Amen" automatically. "It means," she had said, "that you have listened and approve of what was said."

Oh! he did approve of the Bishop's words with every ounce of his being. If only he could believe, as the Bishop so clearly did, that he deserved to be gathered to the Lord's bosom!

At last, they did seem to be making progress against the water, and they pumped with renewed vigor. Gradually, the pitching and rolling began to subside, too. At long last, the captain came to say they could leave the rest of the clean-up work to the sailors.

"We have sent the devil's water back into his teeth!" the captain said.

"We are delivered from evil," said the Bishop.

"Amen and amen," said Charles.

15 | Arrival at Savannah

On February 5, 1736, the *Simmonds* passed Peeper's Island, the first piece of land belonging to the colony of Georgia. Charles stood as far up in the bow as he could, watching eagerly as the ship nosed into the Savannah River and made its way slowly upstream. He was glad when the ship's captain came to stand beside him, because he had so many questions to ask.

"What are those great, twisted trees with the enormous limbs?" he asked. "And all those black-and-white birds with the bubbling song?"

The captain looked at him with surprise. "Why, you're a regular poet, Mr. Wesley, and you *can* think of something besides sin and salvation. There's some on this ship that'd never believe it!"

"God made the world," Charles said simply. "And this is a part of it I've never seen before."

"Yes," said the captain. "Well, the trees are live-oaks. They're evergreen oaks, and their wood is fine for shipbuilding."

"And the birds?" asked Charles, watching one bird in particular swaying on a reed and singing a tune that rollicked upward like the musical scale.

"Reed birds, I call them," said the captain, "though the Indians call them ricebirds." He pointed deeper into the marsh, where tall gray-blue birds stood motionless. "Those are blue herons," he said. "Much like the storks we have in England. If you look closely, Mr. Wesley, you may see a crocodile, too, along the bank or in the water. They're ugly beasts, with their horny skin."

"What do they look like, besides being ugly?" asked Charles.

"Like lizards, only a hundred times bigger than any we have in England. They have long heads with jaws that can bite off a man's leg, and tails that can kill a man with a single lash!"

"If they're that big," said Charles, "surely a man can see one coming and keep his distance!"

The captain shook his head. "They lie low in the water, with just their bulging eyes sticking out. They look like logs. So if ever you decided to swim in the Savannah River —and you will, since it's the only place to take a real bath —you'd be well advised to do it in the early morning, when all the beasts are asleep!"

"And keep my eyes open, even so!" said Charles.

"Even so!"

More of the passengers had come on deck now, and the captain left Charles to speak to some of them. Mrs. Hawkins and Mrs. Welch promenaded by arm in arm, and close behind them came John Wesley. John held a book open in his hands, and his head was bent over it.

"Brother John!" cried Charles. "Come and look at this new land you've come so far to see!"

John raised his head and looked at Charles. "It is not the land I've come to see, but the people I've come to minister unto. Meanwhile," he indicated the book in his hands, "I have this religious biography to finish. The *Life of Lopez*. I recommend it to you."

And John continued to pace the deck, as if unaware of anything but the book he held. Charles looked after him briefly, and once again compared himself unfavorably to his dedicated brother.

The promenading women came around again, and this time they stopped by Charles. He spoke pleasantly to them, ready to tell them what he had learned from the captain. They ignored him as if he were not there, so he turned his back on them and again watched the shore.

"It will be pleasant to get ashore and away from this confining space!" Mrs. Welch said.

"And from these spoil-sport clergymen," said Mrs. Hawkins. "If we had wanted to live the kind of life they'd have us live, we could have stayed in England!"

Charles, less of a crusader than John, determined to say nothing that would let them know he'd heard their conversation. This attitude on his part, though, seemed to infuriate Mrs. Hawkins.

"I told them I'd make them sorry they ever came to this colony," she said.

Mrs. Welch, evidently more timid than her friend, objected mildly. "They came at Governor Oglethorpe's express invitation," she reminded her vengeful friend.

Just then, a sailor cried: "Ahead's Savannah!" and nearly everyone rushed forward to see it for himself. After four months at sea, any sign of habitation was welcome.

The town was on a bluff above the river. As the ship drew close, Charles saw with a pang how different Savannah was from anything he had known before. The houses were mostly of rude, unpainted wood or of what looked like hard red mud, though here and there was a larger, more elegant building.

The streets were either dusty or sandy, because clouds of something were being stirred up by the crowds rushing down to see the ship. Behind the rough village was a great woods. The trees were so thick that the forest looked black.

The Moravians were gathered at one side of the ship, and they sang a hymn of gladness for their safe arrival. As their songs had done all the way across the ocean, so now too they lifted Charles's spirits. He wished he had thought to bring his German flute on deck with him. It would, he was sure, have been a welcome accompaniment for the singers.

Quite a welcoming party was on hand to greet Oglethorpe and the Wesleys. Josiah Hopkey, chief magistrate and governor in Oglethorpe's absence, was there with his niece, Mistress Sophie. Charles was surprised to see that Mr. Hopkey wore a London gentleman's outfit, with a high-waisted outercoat and short, flowered waistcoat, silk knee breeches, and stockings with clocks up the sides.

Mistress Sophie, too, was dressed in the most recent fashion—pointed bodice fitting the figure, very full skirt, and high-heeled silken slippers. Unlike her London counterparts, though, her hair was unpowdered and unheaped; it hung in dark curls to her shoulders.

With the magistrate and his niece was an Indian of huge physique. He was dressed in full chief's regalia, weighed down with ornaments. He stood proudly ready to greet the man who had come to bring his people the Gospel.

"This is Tomochichi, Chief of the Creeks," Mr. Hopkey said to John.

The chief inclined his head just slightly, and Charles was astonished to hear him say in perfect English, "I am deeply pleased to meet you!"

Pretty Mistress Sophie took Charles's arm.

"You seem surprised that Tomochichi can speak our mother tongue," she said. She laughed softly. "He speaks it better than many others in Georgia. Savannah itself is a mixture of German, French, Spanish, and Indian, Mr. Wesley—and English, of course."

Charles was momentarily distracted by the crowd of Moravians, who were being greeted wholeheartedly in German by others obviously of their own sect.

"That's Parson Spangenberg and his flock," said Sophie. "They're building a very large brick church in town. It will have a fine organ to accompany the very fine choir."

Charles's heart began to beat faster when he heard Sophie's words. "Are you fond of music, Mistress Sophie?" he asked.

"Oh yes!" she said. "I play the harpsichord. And you, Mr. Wesley?"

"I learned to play the organ when I was at Westminster School," Charles said, "and I have my flute with me now."

Sophie's eyes shone. "You will have to come to my house, and we can play together!" she cried.

John touched Charles's arm. "Mr. Hopkey is ready to drive us to the Inn," he said.

He bowed to Sophie, who curtsied to him.

The magistrate's coach took Charles and John to the Public House, a huge building made of hewn-pine logs. Next to it was the church, roughly structured from unpainted planks, which were chinked with mud.

Inside, the Public House smelled like public houses anywhere, or so Charles thought. The odors of English ale, of pork and cabbage, hung heavily on the air. The landlord, a big man with his sleeves rolled up, came to meet his guests.

"Each has his own room?" Josiah Hopkey asked, looking at the landlord.

"Oh, yes, sir, just as you ordered, sir!" said the man. "And each his own body servant, too, sir!"

Josiah Hopkey nodded. "Then all's as should be," he told the brothers. "The landlord will show you to your rooms, and I'll say farewell for now."

Charles was delighted with his spacious room which he didn't have to share, particularly after four months of being crowded on the *Simmonds*. He was even ready to accept the services of the colored man, who started to unpack for him as soon as his trunk was delivered.

John, Charles soon discovered, was not at all happy with the luxurious arrangements. In particular, he would not allow the Negro to wait on him at all.

"I am used to waiting on myself," he told Charles. "I do not propose to change my ways in that respect now!"

Charles objected. "It seems to be the custom around here," he said, "and I think we should fall in with it."

John looked at him coldly. "You always have been ready to 'fall in' with things that suited you," he said.

To Charles's surprise, John's words made him think of pretty Sophie Hopkey and of her promise that they would make music together.

"I had not expected to find things to suit me in Savannah," he said, "but I find several things I think I am going to like!"

John looked at him more severely than before.

"I intend to preach against frivolity," he said. "Will you be one to whom I must preach first?"

16 First Hymns

Charles had to devote a good deal of time to doing secretarial work for Governor Oglethorpe, but whenever he could, he visited Sophie Hopkey. The spell of the Moravians' music continued to enthrall him, and his head was full of tunes that must find expression. Fortunately, Sophie was delighted to have him compose on her harpsichord.

John, too, was under a spell, but his was the sense of mission implanted by the Society for the Propagation of the Gospel. He objected to Charles's spending so much time at the Hopkey home, afraid that he was setting a bad example for the other colonists.

"How do you suppose it looks, having you frittering away your time in the home of a pretty young woman?" John demanded.

"But I'm not frittering away my time!" Charles protested, honestly bewildered by the accusation. "On the contrary, I am discovering how I can best bring the Gospel message to the people hereabouts!"

"By playing the organ and singing?" scoffed John, knowing that Sophie had received a new organ from London and that Samuel had sent Charles some organ music by the same ship.

"Yes!" insisted Charles. "Brother John, these people are not desolate and downtrodden, like the poor we visited in Oxford. They are free to live as they like, and they will not take it kindly if we try to force religion upon them."

"And what would your plan be?" asked John, in a disinterested voice.

Charles knew his brother didn't really expect an answer, but he was ready with one anyway.

"To lead them gently toward it," he said. "Come see for yourself tonight, Brother John. There will be a gathering at Mistress Sophie's house."

From his seat at the organ, Charles saw John when he arrived that evening. John's face looked grim and disapproving, as if he had just swallowed something bitter, and his expression grew even more gloomy as he looked around the room.

The fellow guests, Charles realized, were the well-to-do of Savannah, but he knew they were even more in need of something to cling to than other less fortunate-appearing people. But surely John knew this, too. Hadn't he said he intended to preach against frivolity?

Conscious that he had to convince John of the very real contribution music could make to their mission, Charles chose music written specifically for churches. As he played parts of Bach's *Magnificat,* he remembered the thrilling moment in Westminster Abbey when he had first heard it. How can John fail to be moved by it?

John's lips were still set forbiddingly, though, when Charles's fingers were quiet on the keyboard. Charles took a deep breath. He had to make a final try.

He got up and bowed to his audience.

"Now, by your leave," he said, "I would like to run over something modest of my own." He saw Mistress Sophie smiling at him encouragingly, and her smile offset the disapproving frown that had grown still deeper on John's forehead. "The King's favorite composer wrote the music."

A gasp of delighted anticipation arose from the crowd. George Frederic Handel, though German, was the Court Musician of England.

"I am told that Mr. Handel intends to write a whole oratorio, into which he will fit the selection I will play now," Charles continued.

The audience clapped encouragingly. Charles sat down again at the organ. He began to play and to sing his own words to the music. When he had finished, his listeners were absolutely quiet. Charles could see they were intensely moved by the rendition, and that John looked as if the message had gotten through to him too.

His heart pounding with gratitude, Charles decided to drive the message deeper still. He beckoned to Sophie, who came to take his place at the organ. Then he stood and held up his arms.

"I will sing the words, and you sing after me."

Line by line, the audience followed Charles's lead. By the time they had reached the last verse, the room was alive with song, and John was singing, too.

> I know that my Redeemer lives
> And ever prays for me.
> A token of his love he gives,
> A pledge of liberty.

On that transcendent note, the evening came to a close. Charles and John walked back to the Public House together. Charles waited for John to make some comment, but he said no word at all.

"Well, Brother John?" asked Charles, when he could stand the silence no longer.

"There does seem to be definite value in song," John admitted. "Even I was drawn to raise my voice, as you must have noticed."

They were passing the new Moravian church site as he spoke. The moon had set, but by the dim starlight Charles could just see the gesture of John's arm toward the building.

"Perhaps that is one reason why our German-speaking friends are so successful in attracting converts."

There was a trace of bitterness in John's voice, occasioned, Charles was sure, because the Moravian church was so much larger and finer than the church where he preached to an almost hostile congregation.

"I haven't a doubt that is the reason," said Charles, "or at least one important factor."

"But these people are at least civilized," said John. "If ever I can get on with my plans for working with the Indians, and you help me, you would have to forget music. Those savages aren't ready for Bach and Handel!"

"Maybe not for Bach and Handel," agreed Charles, "but they, too, could be moved by music. Why, 'Music hath charms to soothe the savage beast,' Brother John!"

"Did you think that up just now?" asked John, the disapproving tone back in his voice.

"No," said Charles. "That was first said by a friend of Brother Samuel, William Congreve."

"Oh," said John. "One of the literary men who had the freedom of Westminster. I think, Brother Charles, you would have been better fitted for this life if you had been schooled, like me, at Charterhouse."

"Perhaps," said Charles, conscious that he was glad he had his days at Westminster to remember.

"You know," said John, just before they reached the Public House, "Tomochichi presented me with a side of venison—"

"Which you immediately gave away," reminded Charles, "vowing that you would abstain from flesh and spirits as an example to the colonists."

"Just as I stove in the rum casks that were delivered by our ship," added John, "so that the colonists would be protected from temptation. But in that, Brother Charles, I was only anticipating the Governor. After all, it is he who has clamped a ban on all spirituous liquors, not I."

"Nevertheless, it is a ban for which we are blamed," said Charles.

"Blame from the people is unimportant, if it is not deserved," said John.

John started into his room, no doubt thinking he had had the last word. Charles, however, was not ready to abandon the conversation at that point. Uninvited, he followed John.

"There is something you want to say?" asked John.

"Yes," said Charles. "I've said it before, but I have to say it once more."

"You sound censorious," said John.

"I think we should go along with what is customary as much as we can," said Charles. "Besides that, I think you should go to Tomochichi. He is expecting you to preach to his band. *They* are ready and willing to be converted."

"So," said John severely, "because that job would be easier than this, you think I should do it first?"

"No," said Charles. "Because you made a promise."

His shoulders were sagging now and he felt whipped, for he had not succeeded in convincing John of anything.

"You could go to Tomochichi," Said John.

Charles stared at him. "I'm not the one they want!"

"If Governor Oglethorpe will release you, I think you should go," said John. "Now, I really must insist that we say 'goodnight.' It is late, and as you know, I rise early."

"So do I!" cried Charles, his pride stung.

Governor Oglethorpe, however, had plans for Charles that did not leave time for him to visit the Creek camp. He sent a messenger at dawn the next morning to tell Charles they would be leaving for Frederica as soon as Charles could pack. The new church was ready to be dedicated.

Frederica was many miles south of Savannah, nearly a three-day trip on horseback. The route was along an Indian trail, through dense forests and clutching swampland. The clop! clop! of the horses' hoofs was sometimes punctuated by the howls of wolves and the snarl of panthers. Their guide kept a musket ready across his saddle bow, so he could shoot immediately if need be.

Charles felt quite desolate at the sudden disruption of his life. He had grown quite accustomed to his comfortable quarters in the Public House, to being waited on by the colored servant, to the soul-satisfying hours at Sophie's harpsichord or organ. Moreover, he was unused to riding horseback, and he never before had slept on the ground.

He was, however, determined to adapt himself to conditions he could not change. To keep up his spirits, he sang as he rode along, even composed a dedication hymn for the first service in the new church. He pounded out the rhythm to it on his horse's broad rump.

"It's finished!" he said finally to Oglethorpe and to Benjamin Ingham, who was going to be the pastor of the new church.

"Well, let's hear it," said Oglethorpe.

Charles took a pitch pipe from his pouch to set the note for himself. Then he began to sing.

A charge to keep I have,
  A God to glorify;
A never-dying soul to save,
  And fit it for the sky!

Before long, the others had learned the hymn, and the three of them sang it together as they rode the last miles toward Frederica.

17 Misunderstanding Between Friends

Frederica was far cruder than Savannah. It was really just a village of palmetto huts and tents, the only hewn-surface building being the one-room church. The church served as storehouse and as the general assembly house for the settlers, a fact which somewhat shocked Charles.

"A church is a holy place," he said to Benjamin Ingaham. "How can it serve secular interests as well?"

Ingaham raised his eyebrows. "How you do blow hot and cold, Friend Charles," he said.

"What do you mean?" asked Charles.

"You've been following secular interests in Savannah, haven't you? It wasn't only religious music you played on Mistress Sophie's harpsichord, was it? Or only religious thoughts you had when you looked at her pretty face?"

"There's nothing wrong with looking at a pretty face," said Charles, "but I think of Mistress Sophie entirely as a friend, Benjamin—less good a friend than you, whom I have loved for many years."

Ingaham looked at Charles as if to make sure he was serious. Then he smiled a smile of true sweetness, and laid his arm across Charles's shoulders.

"I should know better than to listen to the idle gossip of the town," he said, "and to the insinuations of our acquaintance, Delamotte."

Charles was silent, remembering that it was Delamotte

who had, on the ship, pointed out the sly maneuverings of Mrs. Welch and Mrs. Hawkins.

"Together," Ingaham went on, "you and I can bring true religion to this wilderness."

Ingaham was the official chaplain of the frontier settlement, Charles officially only secretary to Governor Oglethorpe. However, with Ingaham's blessing, Charles soon regarded himself as equally responsible for the spiritual guidance of Frederica. Indeed, Charles became more insistent on proper church form than even John might have been in the circumstances.

The people who were settling Frederica were the most lawless of the colonists. They wanted nothing so much as to be allowed to go to the devil in their own manner. Charles's strict churchmanship was completely contrary to their desires. He insisted especially on the keeping of the fourth commandment:

> Remember the sabbath day, to keep it holy. Six days you shall labor, and do all your work; but the seventh day is a sabbath to the Lord your God; in it you shall not do any work.

It was on this point that Charles ran into serious trouble. The first person caught breaking his ruling was Dr. Hawkins, who went hunting for game on a Sunday. Charles had the doctor confined in the guardhouse for a week, making an example of him.

To this act, even Benjamin Ingaham objected.

"Friend Charles," he said, "Dr. Hawkins is the only medical man in the settlement."

"He broke a primary law of the Church," said Charles. "I cannot make an exception of him."

"Why not?" asked Ingaham, soberly. "Have you not heard that law is sometimes better honored in the breach than in the slavish following?"

"I have heard it," said Charles.

"And you do not think this is the time to prove it?"

"If I am to make an exception of the very first case of Sabbath-breaking, I am lost," insisted Charles.

The Governor was bewildered by Charles's stand, but did not reverse Charles's decision. The result was that several people who needed the doctor's attention had to go without it, and the hue and cry against Charles grew loud and threatening. Loudest of all in her complaints was Mrs. Hawkins, the doctor's wife.

She was, of course, the same woman who, before they left the ship, had sworn to make Charles sorry he had come to Georgia. Charles had almost forgotten that threat, because she had left Savannah immediately after her arrival.

He remembered it, though, when he encountered her at the entrance to Governor Oglethorpe's headquarters. She flashed such a burning look of hatred at him that he felt scorched by the contact. He didn't know what she had said to the Governor, but almost at once Oglethorpe's attitude toward him changed.

Coming to Georgia as Oglethorpe's secretary, Charles expected to live with him, or at least to be provided with the necessities by him. Consequently, Charles had brought nothing from England with him but his clothes and some books. In Savannah, his expectations had certainly been proved correct.

In Frederica, however, he had so far been given only a palmetto hut in which to shelter himself. Oglethorpe kept promising him more conveniences, but they were never delivered.

So long as the weather was dry, Charles could stand sleeping on the earth, as he had on the trip to Frederica. However, soon after the trouble over the doctor's imprisonment, the spring rains came and the floor of Charles's hut was wet and cold. He sent a message to Oglethorpe, asking for a bedstead and for a kettle so he might make hot tea.

Oglethorpe sent back word that there were no bedsteads

or kettles to spare. Unable to believe the Governor would lie, Charles accepted this answer and tried to get his needs from other colonists. They, of course, knew the truth of the matter (that Charles had lost favor with Oglethorpe) and they welcomed the chance to make the "overly holy" man suffer.

They not only denied him the simple things he asked, but they made his life even more miserable by all sorts of petty persecutions. The woman who had heretofore done his laundry sent back his clothes unwashed. The man who brought his food came now with only watery soup.

Charles was willing to accept all such actions, thinking perhaps the Lord was putting him on trial, but the illness that had plagued him during his days of self-denial in Oxford returned to him full force.

Benjamin Ingaham was away when Charles's troubles with the Governor came to a head. When he returned, he went straight away to Charles's hut, where the poor neglected man lay burning up with fever.

"Oh, my poor friend, what has brought you to this sad pass?" cried Ingaham.

Hardly able to talk through his dry, cracked lips, Charles painfully croaked a few words of explanation.

"Has Dr. Hawkins seen you?" asked Ingaham.

"He knows I am ill, but he will not come," said Charles in a hopeless tone. "The Lord is chastening me. I have hoped and prayed to die, but the Lord does not think me fit to take."

Ingaham raised a hand as if in protest, then laid it gently on Charles's head, smoothing back the sweat-dampened blond hair. "The Lord is not vengeful," he said.

"Oh!" cried Charles. "I long to see my brother John!"

Ingaham's face was full of sympathy.

"I will go to Savannah myself to get him!" he promised. "Meanwhile, have faith that the Lord will see you through this time of trial."

"I hope He will," said Charles, "at least until I have seen Brother John again."

John arrived in Frederica on April 10, bringing with him things to make his sick brother comfortable. From John's reassuring presence, Charles gained enough strength to totter with him into the woods where they could talk without fear of being overheard. He poured the story of his woes into John's sympathetic ears.

"Charles, Charles!" said John, when Charles had finished. "To suffer in silence is a luxury you cannot afford. Why did you not ask Mr. Oglethorpe for an explanation?"

"Was not my manner of life explanation enough?" cried Charles, almost weeping from the relief of having unburdened himself.

"Evidently not," said John. "Well, we shall go back to your hut, now. You must rest, and I must go to see the Governor."

While John had his interview, Charles slept comfortably for the first time since his arrival in Frederica. When his brother returned, therefore, he felt much refreshed and ready to hear what John had to say.

"Mrs. Hawkins bore a tale to the Governor that I am certain is untrue," John said. "She told him that you had tried to make love to her, a married woman, not only on the ship but here in Frederica as well."

"He *believed* her?" cried Charles.

"Mrs. Hawkins is a very persuasive woman," John said, "as I know to my shame."

"You believed she was interested in having you save her soul," Charles said, "but the Governor is a more worldly man than you are, Brother John."

"I think I have convinced the Governor that you are innocent of wrongdoing," said John. "He wants to see you, as soon as you are able to go to him."

Charles lay back wearily. "Perhaps tomorrow," he said.

"Not tomorrow!" said John. "I will do all the duties I

know you have had to neglect while lying here ill. You rest and regain your strength."

As always when John was in control, Charles became a passive follower. For the next week, he let John shoulder all his neglected tasks.

John spent whole days catching up on the correspondence that had accumulated during Charles's disgrace and illness. He conducted the necessary church services, even using the pewter chalice and paten that had been his brother Samuel's contribution to the Church.

"Well," said John, when he had tirelessly cut through the mountain of unfinished work, "you are well, now, and I must go back to my charge in Savannah. But first you must promise me you'll go to the Governor."

"I'll go tomorrow," said Charles.

Charles's interview with Oglethorpe was difficult for them both, because both felt they had failed to act as Christians should. Neither had gone that extra step that might have brought understanding.

"But how," wondered Charles, "could you believe I would do the things I was accused of doing? Did you give no thought to my former life and my reason for coming here to Georgia?"

"I believed you were sincere in all your life before," the Governor assured him, "but in Savannah there was talk about all the time you spent with Mistress Sophie—"

Charles felt uneasy, remembering that Benjamin Ingaham, too, had questioned his relationship with Mistress Sophie.

"And," the Governor continued, "I often saw you stop and speak to Mrs. Hawkins on the street here in Frederica. So when she came to me with her tale—well, I had to suppose that you had never been exposed to a woman of her sort before, and had not the strength to resist her."

"But you do believe me when I say there is no truth in the slander, do you not?" persisted Charles.

"I believe you," said Oglethorpe, "but I have to tell you I do not believe you are suited for life here."

Charles's face lost all the color it had regained since his illness. "You are dismissing me?" he cried.

"No, no," said the Governor. "I would not do that to you, particularly after what you have suffered so needlessly."

"Then what do you mean?"

"We will go on as we did before our trouble for a little while. Then, in a few weeks, I will have dispatches ready to send back to England. I want them to be delivered personally."

Charles's heart gave a great leap. "And you want me to be the bearer?"

The Governor nodded. "You will not object to returning to England as my emissary, will you, Mr. Wesley?"

"Indeed not!" said Charles. "I should welcome the chance to see my family again. When will you wish me to return to Georgia, sir? Whenever the Trustees have prepared their answers to your missives?"

The Governor looked a bit confused.

"If you really want to come back," he said slowly, "we'll find a place for you in Savannah. In any case, Mr. Wesley, I respectfully urge marriage upon you. You would find in the married state certain—protection—that would likely prevent any such unpleasantness as you have experienced here."

"I shall take what you say under advisement," said Charles.

After that, things happened as the Governor had arranged, and on July 26, 1736, Charles set sail for England.

18 "You're a Hypocrite, Charles Wesley"

The Frederica episode had shattered more than Charles's health. It had shattered his faith in his fellow man and, worse still, his faith in himself. More than anything in the world, now, he needed something to cling to. Perhaps he could find it in resumption of the methodical routine both he and John had practiced on shipboard before.

The *Hannah,* he knew, was not a passenger ship like the *Simmonds.* A great deal of her deck space was given over to pens of live animals—sheep and hogs and fowl of various kinds. Therefore, when Charles looked around the tiny sittingroom that first evening at sea, he certainly did not expect to find anyone he knew.

To his surprise, however, he heard someone call his name.

"Charles Wesley! By all that's holy, what do you do aboard this modern Noah's Ark?"

A young man came toward Charles with hand outstretched. Charles recognized him as a self-styled disciple of John's, a man named Appee.

"I carry messages from Governor Oglethorpe to the Colony Trustees back in London," said Charles. "And what do you, sir?"

"Oh," said Appee, "illness in my family necessitates the trip."

Charles, ever ready to comfort the sorrowful, said immediately, "I will pray for the recovery of the invalid, if God be willing."

Appee looked him over shrewdly. "Looks to me as if someone ought to pray for you. Perhaps the sea air will prove beneficial."

"Perhaps," said Charles, somewhat taken aback by Appee's offhand manner.

"Was life in Frederica that much worse than in Savannah?" Appee persisted. "We all wondered, when your brother John was summoned to take a hand!"

"I was ill," said Charles, "and I longed to see my brother."

"I, for one, was surprised to hear you'd called for him," said Appee. "I thought you'd be glad to be out from under his shadow."

"I was ill," repeated Charles. "Was it so unnatural to want my brother at my bedside? Aren't you, in fact, going all the way back to England on a similar errand?"

To that question, Appee seemed to have no ready reply, and shortly both men went to bed.

The next day, Charles rose early. After remaining for some time on his knees in prayer, he arose and reached for his Journal. He intended to set down in it the schedule by which he planned to order his life on shipboard. The Journal opened, though, at a page he had written in Frederica, and in spite of himself Charles reread it:

> Mrs. Welch grows more and more like Mrs. Hawkins. Declares she will not longer be "priest ridden," jests about prayer.

Charles put his head in his hands. Oh, there were warnings of trouble before Mrs. Hawkins went to Oglethorpe with her tale, warnings he himself had set down in black and white. He had accused John of blindness. Why had he not had the wisdom to see himself?

He put down his Journal and reached instead for his Bible, the same well-worn book he had consulted at Oxford when Samuel had accused him of leaving God out of his life. Somewhere there was a passage about not seeing clearly.

He found it in the same chapter of *Matthew* that had reminded him about the narrow and wide gates:

> Why do you see the speck that is in your brother's eye, but do not notice the log that is in your own eye?

He read on, cringing at the words that followed, feeling as if the Lord was speaking just to him in saying: "You hypocrite—"

He closed the Book much chastened in spirit, and left the cabin to go in search of Appee. Perhaps with Appee he could have some uplifting conversation, since in Savannah Appee had claimed to be a follower of John's.

For some days, Appee seemed indeed to be just the companion Charles needed. He was willing to try the methodical life, even appeared to benefit by it. Charles began to feel as he had at Oxford, when another man was convinced and became a Holy Club member.

One morning, he could not resist saying so. He set both hands on Appee's shoulders, feeling brotherly toward him.

"Oh, my friend!" Charles cried. "I know I will never cease to be grateful for the Providence that placed us on this ship together."

Appee twisted away from Charles's clasp. "Well, I've ceased now!" he cried.

Charles looked honestly bewildered. "But we've had so many rewarding talks. Did I say something that offended you? I assure you—"

"*You* offend me!" Appee answered bitterly. "The things you do you do to prove to yourself how holy you are. Every time you say a prayer, every time you go without a meal in the name of fasting, every time you talk to me about the need for strict discipline in life—every time you do any of that, you think you're piling up stepping stones to heaven!"

Charles's mouth trembled, but to save his life he could not say a word. His silence seemed to infuriate Appee even more.

"The fact of the matter is, you're a hypocrite, Charles Wesley! Now, get away from me!"

Charles walked away from Appee with the step of an ill man, and in truth Appee's words had made him ill. His stomach, always unreliable, soon pained him unbearably. Before much time had passed, he was once again suffering from an attack of dysentery that confined him to his bed.

As he tossed from side to side, Charles was tormented by the accusation Appee had flung at him. He pounded his hard pillow with his fists, trying to beat away the words, but he could not. However cruelly he had had to learn, it was true. He had no faith that God would save him unless he proved himself worthy. He believed he had to, as Appee had charged, "pile up stepping stones to heaven." He had always believed it. Was he wrong?

As the fever took hold of him, Charles seemed to see the words of the hymns he had written in Georgia jump before his eyes:

> I know that my Redeemer lives
> And ever prays for me.

and the most recent one:

> A charge to keep I have,
> A God to glorify;
> A never-dying soul to save
> And fit it for the sky.

Charles wept because he had written those words; he knew they should be so, but he did not feel that God had any reason to care for him, a hypocrite.

At last, Charles fell into an uneasy sleep. When he awoke, he was sure he was dreaming.

"Man the pumps!" came the cry. "Every able-bodied man among you, man the pumps!"

He was not dreaming, though, for the *Hannah* was enduring a storm much like that which the *Simmonds* had weathered. The *Hannah,* though, was far less seaworthy, and her captain, Charles knew, was more often drunk than sober.

"I have to take my turn at the pumps," Charles told himself, though his teeth were chattering and at the same time he was perspiring profusely. "Even if it kills me, I must go."

Down into the bowels of the ship he went, to find that the water was already waist-deep. A few men passengers were already there, helping the seamen at the pumps. As Charles grabbed a handle, a rat came swimming by. One of the sailors made an obscene remark to him, but Charles hardly credited what was said.

The men worked only half-heartedly, and the water continued to rise. In his despair, Charles thought of the similar scene in the *Simmonds,* and he remembered the Moravian Bishop. His heart lifted, and suddenly he was able to pray.

"Oh, Lord, give me the strength to do what must be done!" Then he began to sing the songs that had brought hope to him when the Moravians sang them.

The men about him at first seemed surprised that anyone could think their situation a singing matter. Gradually, though, a few began timidly to join in, and soon they were working with a will.

The storm continued for almost a week. Then, on November 13, the weather suddenly cleared. The wind died completely, and the ship lay motionless on a glassy sea.

The seamen rejoiced in the chance to mend the shredded sails and repair the leaks. Charles rejoiced to watch them go about their chores with a song on their lips, a song he had taught them.

Just as they finished their work, the calm gave way to a fair wind. The sails filled, there was singing in the rigging once more, and the ship again was underway for England.

On Friday, December 3, 1736, the *Hannah* put into port at Deal, England. When Charles reached shore, he fell to his knees.

> O bless the Hand that hath guided us
> through such inextricable mazes!

he cried.

It was the first time he had really given thanks from the depths of his heart.

19 | A Song in His Heart

The next evening, a Saturday, Charles arrived in London. He longed to see his brother Samuel, but Sam was no longer at Westminster School. His patron, Bishop Francis Atterbury, had been banished for his part in the plot to restore the Stuarts to the throne. Samuel, though guiltless, was judged to be unfit to continue in the school that held the reigning king's favor; he had become, just recently, Headmaster of the Grammar School at Twerton.

Charles had been told to go to the home of a former school acquaintance, James Hutton, in Great College Street, Westminster. Hutton's home had become a regular meeting place for one of the little religious societies that were a recent feature of the times in England. Charles, however, was unsure he would be welcomed there, and he walked toward it with dragging footsteps.

London seemed very big, very dirty, and very noisy to him, after the little colonial towns he'd lived in for a year. Coffee shops had sprung up everywhere, ballad-singers seemed to be on every corner, and the streets looked too narrow for all the coaches and wagons that rumbled constantly by.

Westminster, however, Charles realized thankfully, was as he remembered it. The shadow of the great gray Abbey hovered over the area in the same sheltering way. The chimes sounded just as they had the night Charles first arrived twenty years before.

Taking a deep breath, Charles climbed the steps of James Hutton's home and lifted the doorknocker. After just one clap, the door flew open, and James himself peered out.

For a moment he stared at his visitor as if he had seen a ghost. Then with a cry he gathered Charles into an almost frantic embrace.

"Charles! Charles!" he cried. "We were told your ship had been lost at sea!"

The welcome was so overwhelming that Charles felt hot tears of gratitude stream down his face. James Hutton half led, half carried him into the room where a small company was gathered.

"Here is Charles Wesley, miraculously saved from the perils of the deep!" he cried by way of introduction.

Everybody wanted to know every detail of Charles's adventures, and Charles, soon carried away by his love of words, told them what he thought they wanted to hear.

To Charles's astonishment, the admiring treatment he received in the Hutton household was repeated all over London. He discovered that he was a Personage, and as such was lionized by friends and by strangers in high places. Everybody was interested in the colony of Georgia, and all were eager to obtain information from the governor's emissary.

It had been a long time since Charles had received such admiring attention. After the brutal handling he had endured in Frederica, this was as welcome as the calm sea after the hurricane. Once again he became the charming, vital person who had won the title of Captain over the other King's Scholars at Westminster School.

Finding himself the spokesman for a whole new way of life, Charles sought for the words to describe what it was like. He knew he was envisioned as a Christian pastor, and as such should think only charitable thoughts. Oddly enough, he found that he was losing sight of the hardships he had suffered, considering them as incidental to himself and not the sort of thing anyone else would be called upon to endure.

Charles spoke of Georgia, therefore, with all the descriptive power he possessed. He praised the clearness of the streams, the untouched depths of the forests, the fruits and flowers that grew in wild profusion. He made it sound, in short, like the promised land of milk and honey.

Finally, even the Bishop of London sent for Charles, to hear from the young clergyman's own lips what had been reported to him secondhand.

James Hutton was excited about the summons. "This is the opportunity of a lifetime!" he told Charles. "There is no place you cannot go, no position in the Church too high to aspire to, if you get the Bishop of London to sponsor you!"

Buoyed up by renewed faith in himself, Charles went to see the Bishop. The Bishop received him kindly, and he listened as eagerly to Charles's account as everybody else had.

When Charles at last paused for breath, the Bishop asked one question: "Are you seriously considering returning to Georgia?"

A similar question had been put to Charles many times before. He had always answered, quite glibly, "When my health is better, I expect to return." He could not, however, give the same glib response to the Bishop's question, for it differed subtly from the other queries. The Bishop had added the word "seriously."

"I do not know whether I am strong enough to return," he said instead. "Georgia is indeed a land of limitless opportunity," he added, "but it provided me with a trial which I was not equipped to bear."

When Charles finally left the Bishop's Palace, he was in deep mental distress. This distress increased as the days went by, and he withdrew into himself until his friends were first troubled and then alarmed.

To their well-meant offers of help, he replied, "I must work this out for myself. No one can help me."

And no one could, though the Bishop had tried, because Charles did not know any more what he believed. Not even in the miserable days at Frederica had he felt so completely lost.

Then, one January night at a religious meeting in Hutton's home, he met Count Nicholas Zinzendorf. Count Zinzendorf was the man whom the Moravians in Georgia had called their true leader. In 1722, he had offered his estates in Saxony as a refuge for the persecuted Moravian Brethren. They built a town there and called it Herrnhut.

It was the count's purpose that the Herrnhutters should be a group within the Lutheran Church, influencing other Lutherans toward deeper religious experience. They convinced him that this was not a workable plan and that they wished to revive the movement which had all but died during the Thirty Years War. He yielded to their wish and became head of the company of Brethren.

"How does it happen," asked Charles, "that you did not go to America too?"

"Because," said the Count, "I wish personally to spread the views of my church throughout Europe. There are many of us still in the Old World, Mr. Wesley." He smiled a little wistfully. "But I should like to see that new church building in the Pennsylvania community of Bethlehem and the one I am told is in progress in your Savannah."

Count Zinzendorf's words took Charles back in memory to the evening of the musicale at Sophie Hopkey's. He had succeeded that night in convincing John that music could play an important role in every church service. John had even commented, on passing the Moravian church site, that singing might account for the popularity of the Brethren.

"My brother John believes that the use of song is one of the most important ideas of your church," Charles said.

The count nodded. "Our congregations are very fond of part-singing," he said.

Charles was moved to tell Zinzendorf of the example the refugee Moravians had set during the hurricane that buffeted the *Simmonds.*

"Even the little children," he said, "were calm and unafraid, though the other passengers cried and screamed in terror all around them."

"Children have no trouble believing that salvation is the free gift of God," the count said.

Zinzendorf's words shed a tiny ray of light into the dark recesses of Charles's mind, and he grabbed hold of the count's hand in gratitude.

"Then perhaps unbelievers should become as little children!" he cried.

Count Zinzendorf looked at Charles with compassion. "But that is easier in the dream than in the realization," he said.

Nevertheless, the meeting with the Moravian bishop had given Charles a great deal to think about. Perhaps what he needed to do was start over! But where? He could not go back to Epworth; his father was dead and his mother no longer lived there. He could not return to Westminster School. He was, however, assured of a position at Christ Church College, and it was to Oxford he decided to go.

He was accompanied on the trip by Peter Böhler, a protege of Count Zinzendorf's. Böhler, too, was to take up a position at Oxford; he was to preach in Latin twice a day from the college pulpits.

Charles, of course, had studied German and could converse with Peter Böhler either in that language or in Latin. The townspeople of Oxford, however, could speak neither. That put the young Moravian at a serious disadvantage, so Charles offered to teach him to speak English.

The lessons proved only the starting point for the two young men. Afterwards, they stayed together talking, talking, talking. Once again, Charles had something solid to cling to, and he welcomed Peter Böhler with a song in his heart.

20 The One Thing Necessary

Peter Böhler was not just a rock for Charles to cling to. With his round, boyish face and his contented smile, he was a prime example of everything Charles had sensed in the other Moravians. Neither life nor death held any terror for them, and Charles longed to find out why.

"It is simple," Peter said. "I believe in Christ."

"I believe in Christ, too," said Charles.

"If you truly believed that He died for you," said Böhler, "there would be no room in your heart for doubt. Faith in Him is the one thing necessary for salvation."

Charles shook his head. His trust was in a good life lived according to Church of England teaching.

"You are saying," he told Peter, "that the believer of a moment is as worthy of salvation as the worker of a lifetime."

"I am," said Peter.

For days, the two young men debated the point. Charles wanted desperately to have the peace of mind Peter possessed, but the belief that buoyed up Peter's life was contrary to everything Charles had practiced and preached for thirty years.

As happened so often when he was emotionally upset, Charles fell ill. As he recorded in his Journal for February 24, 1738:

I waked in extreme pain, which I thought would quickly separate soul and body.

Once again he felt the terror that this time he would die, and he was gratified when his new friend came to his bedside to pray with him. Afterward he wrote in his Journal:

"Do you hope to be saved?" Böhler asked me.
"Yes!"
"For what reason do you wish it?"
"Because I have used my best endeavours to serve God."

Böhler shook his head, but said no more, just prayed silently. Charles recorded:

I thought him uncharitable, and said so to myself. "What, are my endeavours not a sufficient ground of hope? I have nothing else to trust to!"

Charles did not die, though, and because he did not, he credited Böhler's prayers with helping him. Now he was more than ever in a questioning state of mind, and for relief he turned to writings not religious at all.

He reread some of William Shakespeare's plays, and in *Hamlet* he found a kind of uneasy comfort. Prince Hamlet, he decided, was like himself in many ways, just as weary of the world, just as uncertain in his mind.

Charles's friends in London were begging him to come back to visit; so in April 1738, he went once more to James Hutton's home in Westminster. After ten days there, he once again became very ill, and no doctors seemed to be able to do anything to relieve him.

"Get Peter Böhler," he pleaded, "or else I shall surely die!"

Hutton was shocked to think Charles was putting faith in a man, not in God, but at last he gave in to Charles's feverish request.

Peter Böhler came and took Charles's hand, and once

again Charles recorded the occasion in his Journal:

> He stood by my bedside and prayed over me, that now I might see the intention in this and my late illness.

He convinced Charles, in fact, that it was God's intention that he should seriously consider the doctrine of Faith. Consequently Charles wrote:

> I must examine myself, to see if I truly believe at all. If I do not, I must never cease seeking and longing for belief until I attain it.

All those who regularly attended the weekly religious meetings in the Huttons' home were members of the Church of England and went faithfully to St. Paul's to take Communion. However, Charles had begun to take a lively interest in Moravian teachings. When John, recently returned from his mission to Georgia, began to do likewise, James Hutton's parents voiced strong objections. They told the members to find a new meeting place.

Once again, Charles fell ill. Now he felt sure he was, as he put it, "being tried by God." Not able to walk, he nevertheless wanted to rid the Huttons of him, so he had himself carried to the home of a poor Moravian mechanic, a man named Bray. Charles wrote of him in his Journal:

> He is a simple man, knowing nothing but Christ, yet, by knowing him, knows and discerns all things.

Charles lay upstairs in Bray's home, with his mind at last open and ready to receive some revelation. His feeling of expectation was so great that his friends, too, all began looking for something miraculous to occur.

Charles kept his Journal by his bedside, constantly recording his feelings in it, as he might have recorded the progress of his fever. Some days he felt high hope, the next day great dejection. As he felt, so his friends felt, too. They alternately sang hymns or fell to their knees in despair.

On Wednesday, May 17, John gave him Martin Luther's *Commentary on the Apostle Paul's Letter to the Galations.* Reading it, Charles felt a great lift in his spirits. Paul, too, preached the doctrine of salvation by faith alone, but he stressed a point that Peter Böhler had not. The faith Paul talked about was not a passive faith, but a faith that worked by love. *Love* was the key word; Paul said if one loved, one necessarily did good works *and* lived a holy life.

Once again, though, Charles felt depression descend upon him. Did he—*could* he—love that way?

With a prayer on his lips, Charles went to sleep on the night of Whitsunday, May 21. He awakened near midnight, hearing a voice that said: "In the name of Jesus of Nazareth, arise and believe and thou shalt be healed."

Charles recognized the voice of Mrs. Turner, his friend Bray's sister, but he believed that it was Christ's voice in disguise. From that moment, he did believe.

In the morning, he awoke refreshed and much recovered. He reached for pen and paper and began to write:

Where shall my wandering soul begin?
  How shall I all to heaven aspire?
A slave redeemed from death and sin,
  A branch plucked from eternal fire.
How shall I equal triumphs raise,
And sing my great Deliverer's praise?

Now Charles felt new life in every pore, and saw the world as if it were as fresh as on the day of Creation. The sunshine was like God's smile, the birds His choir, the flowers strewn as a glorious path for Him to walk upon.

And John, seeing Charles now, knew that he himself did not have Faith.

"When," he cried to Charles, "shall I find the Faith that makes your face a glory to behold?"

Charles, so recently delivered from doubt himself, could only say, "When you love enough, you will know it."

On the night of May 24, Charles was sitting alone in his

little room, reading the Bible. There was a sudden sound of feet upon the stairs and the excited clamor of voices, raised in shouts of exultation and snatches of song.

Charles recognized the song as the one he had composed in the exalted moments following his conversion:

> How shall I equal triumphs raise,
> And sing my great Deliverer's praise?

He rose to his feet just as John burst into the room.

"I believe!" shouted John. "I believe!"

And he told Charles all about the moment in the meeting-house near Aldersgate, when he had "felt his heart strangely warmed."

"We were reading," John said, "from Paul's Epistle to the Romans."

Charles looked at his brother in amazement. "It was Paul's letter to the Galatians that started to turn the tide for me!" he exclaimed.

The coincidence struck Charles as truly a sign from God.

It must have struck John in the same way, because he said, "Like Paul, Brother Charles, we must travel about, preaching the Gospel. We must carry the Good News throughout the length and breadth of Britain!"

"We must sing God's praises to all the world!" cried Charles.

And from his lips came tumbling words he could not hold back:

> 'Tis Love! 'Tis Love! Thou diedst for me!
> I hear Thy whisper in my heart.

"I, too!" said John. "As St. Paul said, 'we are more than conquerors through Him who loved us.' "

"And now nothing in all creation," added Charles very softly, "will be able to separate us from the Love of God in Christ Jesus our Lord."

21 At Newgate

John set out at once on his crusade to spread the Gospel throughout Britain, but Charles decided to start his work in London. Though he shrank from the idea, he determined to take up prison visitation again.

"There is no man more in need of reassurance that God cares for him than the man who is condemned to die on the gallows," he told his friends, who tried to tell him other people were more worthy.

Accordingly, one sunny morning in July, 1738, Charles set out on foot for Newgate Prison.

Newgate Prison was in the gatehouse of the principal west gate of London. As Charles beheld its grim outlines, his step faltered. He wanted to turn away, but he forced himself to go up to the turnkey who guarded the entrance.

"What do ye here?" the turnkey demanded, his eyes moving from Charles's smooth blond hair to his neat buckled shoes. "Surely the likes of ye has no relatives in this hellhole!"

"I am a clergyman, come to pray with whosoever will have me," Charles said.

The turnkey snorted. "Don't know whether they'll want ye, but we've ten men sentenced to hang at Tyburn."

"Will you let me in, so that I may go to them?" asked Charles.

The turnkey shrugged, but he unlocked the heavy gate

and let Charles into the gloomy courtyard. Here the walls cast heavy shadows, and the very air seemed cold, though the July day was hot.

Behind him, the outer door clanged shut. Charles clenched his fists to still the trembling of his hands, but he walked toward the inner gate with his head held high. He saw an occasional face in a narrow window, heard an occasional demoniacal scream, but otherwise there was no sign of life anywhere.

The inner gate, however, swung open at his approach, showing that he had been observed through some peephole. Charles entered, and another turnkey questioned him.

"And who did ye come to see?"

"The men who are condemned to hang at Tyburn," Charles said.

Quickly, the turnkey passed his hands over Charles. "Can't have the hangman cheated," he said, explaining his action.

"All I have is a New Testament," said Charles, showing the jailer the little book he held in his hand.

The turnkey cleared his throat nervously. "Don't know how welcome that'll be," he said, "but come along."

He took a torch and led the way. Charles followed him along stone corridors, around sharp corners, and down flight after flight of steps. The lower they went, the narrower the stairs became, until Charles felt as if the walls might come together and squeeze him between. He put out a hand as if to push them back. They were wet and slimy to the touch, and Charles exclaimed involuntarily on feeling them. The jailer turned around, flashing his light on Charles's face.

"Doesn't surprise ye, does it?" he said. "We're below the moat here, and water will seep in!"

Charles said nothing more, so the turnkey smiled grimly and plodded on. At last, they reached the dungeon of the condemned. As they approached the cell, the jailer rattled his keys.

"I've brought ye a treat, lads!" he cried. "A cleric's come to pray for your rotten souls!"

The sneer in the jailer's words was overpowered by the cursing that issued from the prisoners.

"That's no way to talk!" the jailer said.

In the flickering torchlight, the man looked evil to Charles. His eyes seemed to gleam with fiendish glee at the reception Charles was receiving, and he unlocked the cell door with much scraping of the key.

Charles took a step backward as the door was pulled open, but the jailer winked at him.

"They're all fastened to the floor with leg irons," he assured Charles. "Just keep your distance, and ye'll come to no harm."

Charles went in, and once again he heard a door shut behind him. He leaned back against it, taking what comfort he could from the knowledge that no one could come up behind him. He stayed there, waiting for his eyes to become accustomed to the dark. He had trouble breathing, partly because he was afraid, mostly because of the filthy odors that poisoned the air.

"Well, holy man?" snarled a voice.

Charles could see a little now, enough to make out the forms of the men.

"I have come," he said, "to tell you of One who came down from heaven to save lost sinners."

There was an uneasy muttering among the men. Charles took new heart from the fact that they were no longer cursing him.

"Next time I come," he said, "I will bring a candle so that I may read to you. Now, if you will let me, I will pray with you."

The prisoners were silent, and Charles took their stillness for consent. He went down on his knees on the cold, wet floor and began to recite the Lord's Prayer. When he reached the words: "forgive us our trespasses," several of the men said them with him and continued on to the end.

When it was finished, Charles got to his feet and slowly moved from prisoner to prisoner, touching a hand of each. Only one of them drew away from him. To that man, Charles simply said, "My friend," and continued on his way.

The next day, Charles returned to Newgate. This time he brought a candle with him to light the dungeon. Now he could see the men, and they could see him. They stared at him, in fact, clearly amazed that he had actually kept his promise to return.

Charles read aloud from the book of Romans:

> Christ died for the ungodly. God shows His love for us in that while we were yet sinners Christ died for us. Since, therefore, we are now justified by His blood, much more shall we be saved by Him from the wrath of God.

They listened with an interest Charles had not expected, and when he was done, several of them were crying.

The man who had drawn away from Charles the day before cried, "What, was it for me? Did Christ suffer for so poor a creature as me?"

The tears trickled down his cheeks, leaving clean streaks on his dirty face.

Charles gave the man his own kerchief to wipe the tears away. From the fullness of his own new belief, he said, "Even if in your last hour you repent and believe, God will have mercy."

As he spoke, he realized for the first time that he did, like Peter Böhler, accept the doctrine he had told Peter was "scandalous." The believer of a moment *was* on a par with the worker of a lifetime. The one thing necessary was Faith in God's Love.

Day after day, Charles visited the prison, up until the day when the condemned were to be hanged. That morning he prayed with them for the last time.

He stayed with them until the jailers came to take them away. He recorded the scene in his Journal:

> At half-past nine their irons were knocked off and their hands tied. I went in a coach . . . and by half-past ten came to Tyburn: waited till eleven. Then were brought the children appointed to die. I got upon the cart with them . . .

Once again, he reassured them of God's love, but the reassurance was unnecessary. Clearly, they believed that this day they would be with their Lord in Heaven. He wrote:

> None showed any terror of death. There were no tears. All expressed their desire of my following them to Paradise. I never saw such calm triumph.

Hangings were a favorite public sport of the time, more popular even than bear-baiting or cock-fighting. A very large crowd had assembled on Tyburn Field to watch the ten-fold execution. They expected to hear crying and cursing, and when none was forthcoming, they yelled their disappointment.

The men on the death cart did not seem aware of the jeering crowd at all. They had eyes and ears only for Charles. As the fateful moment approached, Charles broke into a song they had sung together before. All the condemned joined him:

> Father of Jesus Christ, my Lord,
> My Saviour and my Head.
> I trust in Thee, whose powerful word
> Hath raised Him from the dead.

Then Charles kissed each one, and got down off the cart. That moment, too, he recorded in his Journal:

> When the cart drew off, not one stirred or struggled for life, but meekly gave up his spirit. Exactly at twelve this happened. I spoke a few words to the crowd and returned home full of peace and confidence in my friends' happiness. *That hour under the gallows was the most blessed hour of my life.*

22 Spreading the Good News

Fresh from his triumphant experience with the condemned men of Newgate, Charles felt he had to tell the world about the saving power of God's grace. He talked to everyone he knew or met, and on the travels he now undertook he met a great many people. Some of them criticized him for talking of religious things outside the pulpit, but most listened eagerly to the Good News.

As often as he could, Charles traveled by horseback, so he would be in close communion with God's natural world. He was a very relaxed sort of rider; he put his steed in the way it should go, then trusted the animal to move onward until checked.

Sitting at ease in his saddle, Charles was free to read his Bible or, as happened more often, to compose hymns. Scarcely a day passed that Charles did not crystallize some experience into verse. It was as if his conversion had released the power of song that had been imprisoned in his unbelieving heart.

Now, too, the teaching of his old schoolmaster, Vincent Bourne, showed its effect. Charles experimented with every type of rhyme and meter, suiting his words to them or the other way around. Through every thought and expression his unquestioning and childlike trust in God shone.

One Sunday in October, 1738, Charles was at Oxford. He went to St. Antholin's Church, where an old Holy Club friend, Robert Kirkham, was the rector. Kirkham was overjoyed to see him, and begged Charles to preach the sermon at Evensong.

"I have no sermon prepared," Charles objected, but Robert Kirkham would hear no excuse.

"Just get up and talk," he said, "as if you were speaking to a group of friends anywhere."

That night Charles did just that, and he found that the Good News he had to tell was more welcome for the informal way in which he told it.

"Perhaps," he told himself excitedly, "this is the best way to reach the people."

Thereafter, he talked from whatever pulpit was offered him, but wherever he preached only his words differed. His message was always the same. Like St. Paul, he spoke only of "Christ and Him crucified for mankind."

As Charles traveled about the countryside, he began to hear of another Holy Club friend again—George Whitefield, the tavern-keeper's son. Whitefield had sailed for Georgia, Charles learned, on the day John Wesley had returned from America. Whitefield, however, had been successful where first Charles and then John had failed. He had won over the unlettered colonists by a type of preaching that appealed to their *emotions*. Now he too was back in England, but he had left behind him a firmly established and flourishing Church.

In England, however, Whitefield had found all the pulpits closed to him. The Church of England bishops were afraid of this young man, who cared nothing for form and ceremony. Since, however, he was determined to preach, he decided to talk in the open air.

This was the story Charles kept hearing over and over: "George Whitefield is preaching in the fields around Bristol. Huge congregations are turning out to hear him!"

The idea was somewhat shocking to Charles, to whom

the pomp and circumstance of the Church of England ritual was very dear. Nevertheless, he listened with growing interest to the repeated tales of Whitefield's success. When in April, 1739, his brother John actually went to Bristol to substitute for Whitefield, Charles instantly began to tell himself that field preaching was probably all right.

On Sunday, June 24, he found himself at Moorfields, with ten thousand people clamoring for him to talk. It was St. John the Baptist's Day, and with that thought Charles found a precedent he felt safe in following. John the Baptist was a voice that cried through the wilderness. Jesus, too, followed his example when He preached the Beatitudes from the mountainside.

Charles looked at the huge crowd, then held up his hand to quiet them. "Jesus said, 'Come unto me, all ye that labor.' "

With those words of promise, a breathless hush fell over the fields. Charles was almost overcome with the need to continue in that same exultant vein, but he kept on talking and his melodious voice enthralled the listening people.

When he had finished speaking, he suddenly knew that the people needed to sing. Of course, he had no organ, no musical instrument to introduce an unfamiliar tune.

"I'll take a folk ballad!" he told himself, and instantly his quick mind remembered one he had heard the coal miners singing the night before.

He hummed it aloud to the listening throng, then announced he was going to teach them new words to sing to it. This he did, making up the lines as he went along.

"Sing, brethren, sing!" he urged them.

A few timid voices joined him at first, then more and more, until suddenly the field rang with a tremendous roll of melody. The people sang because Charles's message had released the hope that was in all their hearts: the hope of a new and better life.

After that day, hymn singing became a permanent part of every service for Charles. He used a hymn to prepare the people for the sermon they were to hear. He used another to release the tension that the force of the Gospel message was likely to build up.

Charles's sermons were like thunderstorms. First came the thunder of the crashing need for repentance of sin. Next was the lightning flash of conviction of salvation. Finally, there came the gentle healing rain of assured forgiveness.

Now that Charles and John had added field preaching to all their other duties, they made an agreement to share their work. In 1739 Charles took up residence in Bristol, while John remained in London. John had bought an old cannon foundry, which had been almost ruined by an explosion. He had it repaired, and then used it as his headquarters.

In the next few years, Charles and John sometimes combined forces to carry the Gospel farther afield. They rode through the Midland countries, forming Methodist Societies in the towns of Birmingham and Sheffield. They traveled beyond Newcastle to the north, down to Cornwall, finally crossing over to Ireland.

Britain at this midperiod of the eighteenth century still had one law for the rich and another for the poor. The downtrodden masses saw no use in living, and yet feared death more than life. For them, the Gospel the Wesleys preached held a promise that they needed desperately to believe.

In his hymns, Charles crystallized his own and his brother's teaching, but he tailored his poems to his audience. He wrote special songs for every group, using words that held special meaning for them alone.

For the iron-workers of Newcastle:

> See how great a flame aspires,
> Kindled by a spark of grace . . .

For the Cornish fishermen:

> Teach me to cast my net aright,
> The Gospel net of general grace . . .

For the rock quarry men of Portland:

> Strike with the hammer of Thy word
> And break the hearts of stone . . .

and so on for the Bristol colliers, the Staffordshire miners, the Irish pitmen, for everyone who labored.

It was not long before the people's new attitude toward life became apparent to all who cared enough to look for it. Everywhere Charles went, he could see outward signs that proved the Gospel message was getting through. The most spectacular evidence of this was in West Cornwall.

Charles and John had visited that district, knowing it was a hotbed of crime. The jails were overflowing there, and the authorities despaired of ever cleaning up the district. The brothers had preached there to all who would listen, and worked individually with any man who wanted personal help. As always, they had stressed that God's love was given freely to all who repented their sins and truly believed, but they had not been sure their preaching would really get through to hearts so thoroughly hardened by crime.

One year later, however, Charles returned to West Cornwall again. What he found out he recorded in his ever-present Journal:

> My heart is joyful, for now not one felon is to be found in their prisons.

He was moved by this, as by almost any experience, to write a song of joy:

Jesus! The Name high over all
In hell, or earth, or sky;
Angels and men before it fall,
And devils fear and fly.

The Orthodox followers of the Church of England had not liked George Whitefield's way of preaching. They liked it even less when the Wesleys began to follow his lead and to preach wherever they wished. And when the clergymen of the villages saw how their congregations were flocking to the fields, they were furious.

The irate clergymen, of course, had custom on their side. They complained, as Samuel Wesley's curate had back when Susanna decided to hold prayer meetings in the kitchen at Epworth, that sermons and sacraments belonged inside church buildings. When the complaints about the "blasphemous conduct" of the field preachers did no good, the local Anglican ministers often led mobs against the Wesleys.

Charles, of course, had been used to persecution since his Holy Club days at Oxford. He had suffered agonies in Georgia, too, but he had long ago convinced himself that without the lesson of Frederica he might never have realized how terribly lacking in Faith he was.

The persecution he now suffered, though, was of a different character. It was instigated by men duly ordained in the Church of England, the institution which was so dear to Charles's heart.

The worst riot against him occurred at Devizes, in February, 1747. The local clergyman had apparently gone from house to house, charging that he had heard Charles preach against the Church. He had gathered together a mob and appeared at the house where Charles was staying.

"Come out, Blasphemer, and show your face!" the rabble cried.

Charles, who even in his Westminster days had never feared a fight, went to the front door. He would have gone out, too, but his friends in the house pulled him back.

"They'd as soon kill you as not!" the friends cried. "What good would come of *that?*"

Charles gave in to their entreaty and stayed where he was, but even so he was hit by a rock that someone hurled through a window.

"Let me go out to them!" he said to his host, when he saw the damage that was being done, "Let me go, else your house will lie in ruins about you!"

The violence of the mob increased. The rioters broke every window and tore off every shutter they could reach. Then they went for the fire engine and deluged the house. The water flooded the rooms, but still the host would not let Charles go.

The water treatment was either the last thing the mob could think of, or the local rector was alarmed at the damage that was being done. Whatever the cause, the persecution ceased and the crowd departed.

That evening, Charles preached to the local Society of Methodists just as if nothing had happened. The next day, when he left town, he was forced to ride between two lines of scowling men, but their fury had been spent or at least subdued. They threw a few stones and many insults, but that was all.

From that experience, too, came a hymn:

> And are we yet alive,
> And see each other's face?
> Glory and praise to Jesus give
> For his redeeming grace!

23 Marriage Problems

In the summer of 1741, Charles visited the country of Wales for the first time. He planned to start his preaching in Glamorgan, of which Robert Jones was the reigning squire.

The squire sent word that he wanted to see Charles, so Charles went to Fonman Castle to visit him. As soon as the two men were together, Jones started to laugh uncontrollably.

Charles went to him, concerned for the man's state of health. "Is anything wrong, sir?" he asked.

Jones caught his breath and wiped his eyes with his kerchief.

"My laughter is inexcusable, Mr. Wesley," he said. "It is just that you are such a surprise to me!"

"How so?" asked Charles.

"I have heard such wild tales about you," Jones explained, "that I expected to find you a crazy-eyed, red-faced, hair-shirted fanatic. Instead, you're the very model of a proper London clergyman!"

"Say, rather, Oxford and Bristol," said Charles, "and you'll not be far wrong. As yet, I have preached little in London."

"Did you attend Oxford, too, perhaps?" asked Jones.

"I did, sir."

In a few moments, the two men discovered that they had been at Oxford at approximately the same time, and Charles only marveled that Robert Jones had not known of the Holy Club's existence.

"Sometimes it seemed that all of Oxford must be ridiculing us," Charles said. "It just shows how one's troubles are magnified in one's own eyes."

"Well," said the squire, "I called you here, thinking to reprimand and silence a troublemaker. Instead, sir, I beg you to make my castle your home, whenever you are in the vicinity."

Charles was happy to oblige, since he found much to admire in the squire, and the two soon became fast friends. Indeed, he won not only Robert Jones but all of Jones's household over to his way of thinking.

Another squire whom Charles met through his association at Fonman Castle was Marmaduke Gwynne, of Garth. Gwynne had always favored Howard Harris, a field preacher who had much in common with the Wesleys, and he found Charles's brand of religion very much to his taste.

Charles knew that Squire Gwynne had several daughters, but he never met any of them until the summer of 1747. On that day, August 24, he met two of them—Becky and Sally. Charles was forty years old, Miss Sally only twenty, but Charles lost his heart to her immediately.

When Charles had left Georgia, Governor Oglethorpe had urged him to marry as quickly as possible. Charles, however, had not met any young lady who seemed worthy of taking to wife. Therefore, he had not objected when John suggested an agreement between them shortly after their mutual conversion. The two brothers solemnly promised each other that they would "neither marry nor take any steps toward marriage *without the other's prior knowledge and consent*."

This action on their part seemed like a wise precaution. Undoubtedly, this need for consultation with each other kept each more than once from taking a rash step that might have led to an unsuitable marriage.

True to his promise, Charles did not speak of his love to

Sally until he had talked the matter over with John. Luckily, when John met her, he approved of Miss Sarah Gwynne. He even encouraged Charles's courtship.

Sally's father, too, was overjoyed at the idea of her marrying an intelligent, religious man like Charles, even though she was rich and he was penniless. Sally's mother, however, voiced an objection.

"I cannot have my daughter marry a man who has no money of his own at all," she said.

Charles, of course, told John of this obstacle to his happiness.

"I love her and do not wish to live without her," he said, "but I have no means of making money."

"You *are* making money," John assured his worried brother. "You forget that I arranged for the publication of some of your hymns. The book is selling very well indeed."

"But will it make me any regular sum of money?" asked Charles, somewhat cheered.

"You are still writing hymns," said John, "and you will continue to do so. You can have two hundred pounds clear now, and I will guarantee that you can count on at least one hundred pounds a year hereafter. Do you think that will be enough to satisfy Mrs. Gwynne?"

"I can but write her and see," said Charles.

He sat down and wrote her immediately, setting forth his financial situation as clearly as he could:

> Till now I neither knew nor cared what my writings were worth, but the book I am now publishing will bring in more than £200 clear . . .

After he had written that much, he stopped and thought for a moment before he took up his pen again:

> Permit me to add one thing more. If, after this, you are satisfied, and you and Mr. Gwynne see cause to give your consent, I would desire Miss Sally might secure her fortune that it might return to her own family.

His heart almost stopped at the idea of Sally's dying, while he himself was yet alive, but he added:

> I seek not hers, but her; and if the Lord should give and take away, I shall want nothing on earth.

Mrs. Gwynne's objection was overcome by Charles's letter as much as by the fact that he was assured one hundred pounds a year, and the marriage day was set for April 8, 1749.

Just as Charles and John were setting out on their journey from Bristol to Garth for the wedding, though, John decided he did not agree to it after all, that it was not right for Charles.

"We shall go to Wales," John said, "for I have promised to preach there; but I will not go to Garth!"

And indeed it seemed John meant what he said. He stopped at several places to preach, and every time he did, Charles felt like crying out: "You're to preach a wedding service, not a sermon on sin!" He was so nervous that his stomach started to bother him again, as it did so often when his emotions were affected.

The wedding day was to be April 8, and at dawn on the seventh they were still at Fonman Castle, miles away from Garth. Charles was almost beside himself with worry and distress, when finally John agreed to go at least to the Gwynne family and talk matters over.

They rode, with Charles pacing them, like wild men. Their horses were all in a lather, but they reached Garth in time for breakfast.

After breakfast, Charles had the chance to be alone with his bride, while John closeted himself with her parents. Neither of the couple knew what went on behind those closed doors, but whatever it was, it worked for their benefit. The next day John himself officiated at the marriage of Miss Sarah Gwynne to Mr. Charles Wesley.

The newly wedded pair spent their two weeks' honeymoon at Garth, with Charles preaching twice a day in neighboring churches. After that, they set up housekeeping in Bristol, and Charles continued to travel out from there, "cheerfully" leaving his bride behind.

This, at least, is how he spoke of his itinerant preaching in letters to his brother John. He had to make John believe that marriage was in no way interfering with the work of Gospel-spreading the two brothers had mapped out for themselves:

> I forgot my wife as soon as I left her . . . and I felt more zeal, more life more power than I have felt for years!

Sally, however, was not so happy to be left alone, and for a while Charles took her with him. She could not stand the hardships that were necessary, though, so she begged Charles to let her sister Becky come to stay with her.

Sally was a very sociable little person, used to a big family and many visitors coming and going. She liked to have people around her and invited many to her new home in Bristol, too. When Charles was home, though, he soon put a stop to Sally's habit of holding "open house."

"Method is everything," he said firmly. "I have always ordered my life, and must insist that ours together be ordered, too."

So he set up a very strict regime for his household, much like the one which he had practiced at Oxford and on shipboard and any place else he had ever settled down. He would rise at four, and spend his mornings in reading or writing. He would spend his afternoons in visiting "ministerially" from house to house. At eight in the evening, the whole family would assemble for prayers and hymn-singing.

Charles ordered his life in this manner, and it satisfied him so completely that he wished his brother John could make a marriage that was as good with a wife that was as submissive.

The Methodist Societies, which he and John had created during the years since their conversion, had all been glad when Charles married so fine and religious a girl as Sarah Gwynne. Like Charles, they wanted John to find a suitable wife, too. John, however, upset things by falling in love with a completely *unsuitable* woman.

Grace Murray was a widow, whose conversion had been brought about through the reading of the same chapter in Romans that had so "strangely warmed" John Wesley's heart at Aldersgate. She had written an account of her conversion for Charles in May of 1740, and it was he who accepted her as a member of the Society of the People Called Methodists.

For many years, Grace was just another Methodist helper. She traveled about with both brothers in the capacity of waiting maid until Charles's marriage. Then she traveled alone with the "saint-like" John, keeping house for him whenever he settled long enough in one place to take up residence.

One time, John chanced to fall very ill. Grace Murray nursed him back to health. Quite understandably, he became more and more dependent upon her, and finally he realized he loved her.

By the time Charles learned about this, however, John had failed to keep the solemn promise he and Charles had made to each other back in 1738. He had asked Grace to marry him without first consulting Charles.

Charles was exceedingly hurt by this lack of faith on his revered brother's part. For twenty years, he had looked up to John, believing his brother could never do anything wrong. Now he had broken a trust that Charles had considered sacred—one, in particular, that Charles himself had honored.

This was more than Charles could bear, and he determined to stop a marriage that he knew was all wrong. Charles accomplished his purpose; he effectively destroyed his brother's romance with a "completely unsuitable" woman.

What John felt about this interference, Charles could only imagine. What he himself felt was easy. John had broken faith in failing to ask his permission before he took "any step toward marriage," and Charles felt completely justified in preventing the nuptials.

Nevertheless, from this time—October, 1749—things were never again the same between the two brothers.

24 | It Cannot Be

The fate of the Methodist Societies was now uncertain. John, their unchallenged leader, had been tried and found wanting in so basic a Christian virtue as keeping faith with his brother. Charles, the second in command, was criticized for the cruel way in which he had punished John's sin, even though the purity of his motive was unquestioned.

As always, Charles needed someone to look up to, someone to guide him. In Epworth, it had been one of his parents; at Westminster, Samuel; at Oxford and in Georgia, John; again at Oxford, Peter Böhler; in their joint evangelism, John once more. Now that John and he were estranged, Charles turned to the person who grew daily more dear to him—his wife, Sally.

Charles delighted now in putting himself under Sally's direction. He began to call her "dearest partner" and to consult her before he took any step. Fortunately, she was a wise as well as loving woman, and she recommended reconciliation between Charles and John "for the good of the Methodist Societies."

Since John had chosen to go on his evangelizing way as if there had been no trouble at all, it was comparatively easy for Charles to do the same. Their paths did not cross very often, and what letters they exchanged could be strictly devoted to the business relating to their common goal. This show of "business as usual" slowly brought the whole situation back to normal, and the Methodist Societies continued to grow and to multiply.

Sally, however, worried a great deal about her husband's health. She knew how hard the constant traveling and field preaching was on him, for he never let weather interfere with his mission. She began to talk of his giving up itinerant preaching in favor of staying in Bristol and carrying on his Gospel-spreading from the pulpit there.

"You can leave the traveling to the younger men," she said. "What else are you training them for?"

Charles had to think about that before he could answer. He and John between them had established Methodist Societies throughout the length and breadth of Britain, just as they had planned. The Societies were full of eager young people, both men and women, who were delighted to spread the Gospel farther afield.

"I worry only because the young people seem so ready to call our way of life the 'new religion,' " Charles said. "They feel no real loyalty to the Church of England, but only to the Society of the People called Methodists."

Such evidence of the possibility of separation from the Church of England greatly bothered Charles. Every time he heard talk of such a schism, he objected

"The Societies are necessary," he insisted, "only as a means of nourishing and sustaining the life of the spirit. I am sure God is working through them to bring renewed strength to the Established Church."

Charles's love for the Church amounted almost to adoration. It stemmed from childhood days, when he was proud to be the son of one of God's spokesmen, happy in the forms and ceremonies he learned at St. Andrew's Church. It had been reinforced by the years at Westminster, where the great gray Abbey had regulated his hours. He would not tolerate any talk of the founding of a separate sect; he considered it blasphemous.

The hymns he wrote during these years stress over and over again his deep love for the Mother Church and his distress at talk of leaving her. Yet this topic was not the only point of trouble between Charles and the Methodist Societies. Another major problem was the influence of Moravianism on them.

Charles, of course, thought highly of the Moravian religion. He knew that without Peter Böhler he might never have been brought to see the Light. He had, indeed, even accepted Peter's doctrine of "instant salvation," promising the condemned men in Newgate that "Even if in your last hour you repent and believe, God will have mercy."

There was, however, one point upon which the Moravians and the Wesleys could not agree. The Wesleys believed that God had given men laws to be kept and commands to be obeyed, and *it was up to them to follow the laws while waiting for God's grace*. The Moravians believed it was of no consequence what men did or left undone; they needed only to be still, for *nothing they did before faith came would be of any importance*.

This doctrine—known as the Doctrine of Stillness—was completely unacceptable to Charles and, he knew, to John also. He could not let the Methodist Societies follow it any more than he could bear to let them break away from the Established Church.

Charles, therefore, felt pulled in two directions. On the one hand, he wanted to make sure the Societies did not stray off the path on which he wished them to go. On the other, he wanted to stay home with Sally and his growing family. His first son, Jackie, born in the spring of 1752, was the pride of his heart.

In November, 1753, Charles heard that his brother was critically ill in London. At once, all the hard thoughts he had had against John melted away, and he sobbed like a heart-broken child.

"I cannot stand the thought of losing him," he cried to his wife. "I must go to him at once and do what I can to help him."

He hired a post chaise and set out for London. He found John very weak, but as eager as Charles to be reconciled.

"At last I can do for you what you did for me in Georgia!" Charles told him exultantly.

He did his utmost to fulfill all John's duties, preaching many times, spending hours consoling members of John's congregations, who were already mourning their leader's death.

The people responded to Charles with great thankfulness, and they began to beg him to stay with them "if God takes John Wesley to his bosom."

This, however, Charles would not agree to do.

"I neither could nor would stand in my brother's place, if God takes him to Himself," said Charles. "I have neither a body, nor a mind, nor talents, nor grace enough for it."

While Charles struggled to fill his brother's shoes in London, he learned that Sally had fallen ill with smallpox. He was almost beside himself with shock, but he knew that he had to be a rock now for both patients to cling to. Back and forth he traveled between London and Bristol. From his heart poured some of the best poetry he ever wrote, as he tried to prepare himself for the loss of both his loved ones.

> Father, I stretch my hands to Thee;
> No other help I know:
> If Thou withdraw Thyself from me,
> Ah! whither shall I go?

Both John and Sally, however, recuperated from their illnesses. Just as Charles was rejoicing, he received another blow. His beloved little son, Jackie, caught smallpox from his mother and died.

How Charles regretted now that he had not taken Sally's advice to leave itinerant preaching to the younger men! He had been home so little with the child that he had not dared show him the great love he felt, for fear that he would bewilder the boy.

This regret he poured out in a poem—"On the Death of a Child":

> Dead! Dead! The child I loved so well!
> Transported to the world above.
> I need no more my heart conceal:
> I never dared indulge my love:
>   But may I not indulge my grief,
>   And seek in tears a sad relief?

While John was ill and Charles completely occupied between London and Bristol, some of the outlying Methodist Societies got out of hand. They demanded separation from the Church of England. They wanted Methodism to be an independent church with its own ministry.

Charles was almost too spent with grief to challenge this strong demand.

"It cannot be," he said to John in bewilderment. "Methodism is *not* an independent religion. It is just God's means of reinforcing the spiritual life!"

"It can be," said John. "Indeed, it may have to be, Brother Charles!"

Charles shook his head unbelievingly. "It cannot be," he said again.

Hoping to hold back the tide of change, he wrote to each of the ministers of the rebelling churches:

> I love thee from my heart; yet rather than see thee a Dissenting Minister, I wish to see thee smiling in thy coffin.

In 1771, Charles moved his family to London. He had two sons and a daughter, who he thought would benefit by living in the capital. They were all gifted children—young Charles and young Samuel both were fine musicians, young Sally a poet like her father. Moreover, Charles wanted to be where he might be some influence in controlling John's bent toward leaving the Established Church.

The die was cast, though, and the Methodist Societies moved closer and closer to separation from the Church of England. On February 28, 1784, John drew up the Deed of Declaration that marked the official beginning of the Methodist schism.

Charles protested, but John told him the move was absolutely necessary.

"Unless I do this," John said, "Methodism will not survive us."

The Deed appointed by name a hundred Traveling Preachers to form the "Conference of the People Called Methodists." It defined their powers and provided for the filling of vacancies that would surely arise.

For Charles, it defined more than all that. It defined the basic difference between his belief and John's. In his Journal, he wrote:

> My brother's first object was the Methodists and then the Church. Mine was first the Church and then the Methodists.

Charles now made every possible effort to plug up what he called the "hole in the dike." He preached from every pulpit. He begged his audiences not to forsake the Church of England.

Nothing he could do or say was of any use, and Charles fell into the very depths of despair. He wrote:

> My brother does not and will not see that he has renounced the principles and practices of his whole life . . . thus our partnership is dissolved. I have lived on earth a little too long, to have lived to see this evil day.

He did not live much longer. On March 29, 1788, he died, protesting to the last "it cannot be!"

By his own choice, he was buried "in hallowed ground" in the old churchyard of St. Marylebone, and his pall was carried by eight clergymen of the Church of England. His brother John was not in London at the time.

Two weeks later, however, John Wesley held a memorial service for his brother in the Foundry Chapel. He mounted to the pulpit, holding his head proudly high. He announced the hymn—one of Charles's most beloved:

> Come, O Thou Traveler unknown
> Whom still I hold but cannot see:
> My company before is gone,
> And I am left alone with Thee . . .

According to the custom, John started to read the first stanza aloud. When he reached the lines "I am left alone," he could not go on. Tears streamed down his face, and he cried uncontrollably.

In the pews below him, everyone else was crying, too. They were overcome by the combined emotions of pity and grief. They cried for the old man "left alone" and for themselves, deprived of their "sweet singer."

The "sweet singer" was indeed gone, but he left behind him over six thousand songs for Methodists—indeed, for all the world—to sing.

The Fifteen Best-Known Hymns of Charles Wesley

A Charge to Keep I Have

Blest Be The Dear Uniting Love

Christ the Lord is Risen Today!

Come, O Thou Traveler Unknown

Come, Thou Long-Expected Jesus

Father of Jesus Christ, My Lord

Gentle Jesus, Meek and Mild

Hark! The Herald Angels Sing

Jesus, Lover Of My Soul

Love Divine, All Loves Excelling

O For A Thousand Tongues To Sing!

O Thou Who Camest From Above

Sing To the Great Jehovah Praise!

Soldiers of Christ, Arise!

Ye Servants of God

Bibliography

ASHTON, JOHN, *Social Life in the Reign of Queen Anne.* London: Chatto and Windus, 1904.

BAILEY, ALBERT EDWARD, *The Gospel in Hymns.* New York: Scribners, 1950.

BOTSFORD, JAY BENNETT, *English Society in the 18th Century.* New York: Macmillan, 1924.

BRAILSFORD, MABEL RICHMOND, *A Tale of Two Brothers.* New York: Oxford, 1954.

FUNSTON, JOHN WESLEY, *The Wesleys in Picture and Story.* Oak Park, Ill.: Kable Bros. Co., 1939.

HARTLEY, DOROTHY, *Life and Work of the People of England in the 18th Century.* New York: Putnam, 1931.

JONES, D. M., *Charles Wesley, A Study.* London: Epworth Press, 1919.

KROLL, HARRY HARRISON, *The Long Quest.* Philadelphia: Westminster, 1954.

MCCUTCHAN, ROBERT GAY, *Hymns in the Lives of Men.* Nashville: Abingdon, 1954.

TURBERVILLE, A. S., *English Men and Manners in the 18th Century.* Oxford: Clarendon Press, 1929.

WESLEY, CHARLES, *The Journal of the Reverend Charles Wesley.* London: Robert Culley, 1909.

WISEMAN, F. LUKE, *Charles Wesley, Evangelist and Poet.* Nashville: Abingdon, 1932.

About the Author

ELISABETH P. MYERS has always been an admirer of Charles Wesley's hymns. At Garrett Biblical Institute in Evanston, Ill., she was able to find the complete Journals of Charles and John and much other material relating to the two Wesleys and their families. After reading this, she set about following in the brothers' footsteps as closely as possible, first through Georgia, then through England and Wales. This biography is the result of her research.

Mrs. Myers has been a children's librarian in her home town of Wilmette, Ill. At present she is a consultant for a large text-book publisher. Her stories and articles have appeared in *Jack and Jill, Grade Teacher, Instructor,* and numerous denominational magazines. She is the author of several other biographies for teen-age readers.